The Tra

Doroth

Other Titles from The Mythopoeic Press

Tolkien on Film: Essays on Peter Jackson's The Lord of the Rings
Edited by Janet Brennan Croft

Sayers on Holmes: Essays and Fiction on Sherlock Holmes
by Dorothy L. Sayers
Introduction by Alzina Stone Dale
Annotated bibliography by Joe R. Christopher

The Pedant and the Shuffly
by John Bellairs
Illustrated by Marilyn Fitschen
Foreword by Brad Strickland

The Masques of Amen House
by Charles Williams
Edited and annotated by David Bratman
Introduction by Bernadette Bosky

Chad Walsh Reviews C.S. Lewis
Preface and bibliography by Joe R. Christopher
With a memoir by Damaris Walsh McGuire

The Travelling Rug
by
Dorothy L. Sayers

with an introduction and bibliography
by
Joe R. Christopher

and annotations
by
Janet Brennan Croft

The Mythopoeic Press
Altadena, California

The Mythopoeic Press is an imprint of: The Mythopoeic Society, P.O. Box 6707, Altadena CA 91003 (www.mythsoc.org). Orders and inquiries may be directed to: The Mythopoeic Press, 920 N. Atlantic Blvd. #E, Alhambra CA 91801.

Printed in the United States of America. First Printing 2005.

Sayers, Dorothy L. (Dorothy Leigh), 1893-1957.
   The travelling rug / by Dorothy L. Sayers ; with an introduction and bibliography by Joe R. Christopher ; and annotations by Janet Brennan Croft.
      p. cm.
   Includes bibliographical references.
   ISBN-13 978-1-887726-10-8
   ISBN-10 1-887726-10-1
   1. Women domestics--Fiction. 2. Haunted houses--Fiction. 3. Poltergeists--Fiction. I. Title.
   PR6037.A95T73 2005
   823'.912--dc22

                        2005022211

Cover design by Eleanor M. Farrell. Set in Palatino Linotype and Maiandra GD.

Table of Contents

In Intention: Sayers's Third Serial Detective

Joe R. Christopher

The readers of Dorothy L. Sayers's books will know Lord Peter Wimsey, the detective protagonist of eleven novels and twenty–two short stories, and Montague Egg, the working class (or, in American terms, lower middle-class) wine salesman who also solves mysteries and appears in eleven short stories. But they may not know that Sayers started a third series, featuring a lower-class female protagonist and crime solver. She is the subject of this book. Let us, however, begin with some background.

Dorothy Leigh Sayers was born in Oxford, England, in 1893, the only child of an Anglican clergyman and his wife. When she was four and a half, the family moved to a parish in Bluntisham, Huntingdonshire (in what is called in England the fenland of East Anglia). There Sayers grew up. After being educated at home (with her father teaching her Latin, for example), in January 1909 she began attending a boarding school and, evidently after an illness which removed her from school at the end of

1911, studied at home with tutoring by correspondence from a teacher at the school. Then she went, on scholarship, to Somerville College, Oxford University. After her years at Somerville (with, in American terms, a major in French), she held several different jobs—one of them as a secretary at a school in France in 1919-1920. It is while she was there that the first recorded mention of her writing detective stories occurs.

Sayers told Eric Whelpton, her supervisor, when he teased her about reading crime stories, that she and some Oxford friends were considering forming a syndicate to write detective stories. The three friends were Michael Sadleir and G.D.H. and Margaret Cole. Sadleir was later best known for his collection of nineteenth-century fiction, but he was not a writer of mystery novels. G.D.H. Cole was co-editor of the first *Oxford Poetry*, published in 1915, in which Sayers's "Lay" appeared, so he and Sayers had been acquainted for at least five years. The Coles are famous for their sociological studies and their support for Fabian Socialism, but they also wrote a series of mysteries—he wrote the first alone, and then they listed both names on the subsequent twenty-nine novels and seven books of short stories. They seem to have each written separate novels and stories, but the dual by-line was helpful in focusing attention; they also shared some serial detectives. Unfortunately, the general critical agreement is that their mysteries are only average for the period. Sayers, however, mentions as fairly successful G.D.H. Cole's use of a woman—Joan Cowper—as a detective in *The Brooklyn Murders* (1923); since that was a book in which Superintendent Henry Wilson was the official detective, no doubt the book involved amateur vs. professional investigations.[1] Sayers included a story by the Coles in her *Second Omnibus of Crime* and was involved in a collaboration with them and others—as members of the Detection Club—on *The Floating Admiral* (1931). Sayers also reviewed five of her friends' novels during her stint of mystery reviewing for *The Sunday Times*.

The idea of a syndicate explains why Sayers wrote a trial version of a Sexton Blake story (probably in 1920, during the period in France). The Blake stories began in a boys' paper in 1893; like the Nick Carter stories in dime novels and pulp magazines in America, the approximately 4000 Blake stories have been written by a large sequence of authors. Sayers commented in her introduction to *The Omnibus of Crime* that the series "present[s] the nearest modern approach to a national folk-lore, conceived as the center for a cycle of loosely connected romances in the Arthurian manner."[2] Sayers's own Sexton Blake account introduced, as a minor character, Lord Peter Wimsey—however, he was there the "[y]ounger son of the Duke of Peterborough," not the younger brother of the Duke of Denver, as in the published works.[3]

The syndicate formed by Sayers and her friends did not work out; but in the next year, 1921, while Sayers was working at various jobs in London, in a letter she mentions the beginning of the plot of the first Lord Peter novel, except that the corpse in the bathtub is that of a woman, not, as in *Whose Body?*, a man. The novel was published two years later, in 1923.

Soon after she began selling her novels, Sayers began writing commercial stories. The first Lord Peter story published was "The Problem of Uncle Meleager's Will" in *Pearson's* in 1925. Sayers's first book of short stories was entirely of Wimsey tales: *Lord Peter Views the Body* (1928). But the second collection, in 1933, *Hangman's*

Holiday, while including some Wimsey stories and some miscellaneous, had six stories about a new serial detective, Montague "Monty" Egg. None of the Egg stories had been previously published. Lord Peter is a wealthy member of the leisure class, if that is not a redundancy. Egg, in contrast, goes from locale to locale in his salesman's rounds, he quotes rhymed aphorisms from the *Salesman's Handbook*, and he dresses well, including a "smart trilby," to impress his customers. Victor Gollancz, Sayers's publisher and a socialist (he was one of the founders of the Left Book Club), wrote her that he liked the new detective.

In the published letters, Sayers does not say what caused her development of a second serial detective. No doubt part of the impulse was simply to try something new; perhaps part was that she had lived much of her life in Egg's milieu—and writing about it was therefore easier than about Wimsey's. (Her early background was not lower middle class, but her life in London certainly was.) But it is also possible that she had even then heard comments that the Lord Peter saga was "snobbish," as Colin Watson suggested in his *Snobbery with Violence* (1971):

> Of course she was snobbish: the fun she allowed herself in putting into Bunter's mouth [Bunter being Lord Peter's man] the pomposities of a late Victorian butler is altogether innocent of social criticism, while she treated Wimsey, even at his most inane, with an auntie-like indulgence that amounted almost to fawning.[4]

Perhaps Sayers chose to show that her imagination was not wedded to upper-class daydreams. In fact, Sayers had said in the essay "How I Came to Invent the Character of

Lord Peter Wimsey," "Lord Peter's large income . . . I deliberately gave him. . . . After all it cost me nothing and at that time I was particularly hard up. . . . When I was dissatisfied with my single unfurnished room I took a luxurious flat for him in Piccadilly. When my cheap rug got a hole in it, I ordered him an Aubusson carpet. When I had no money to pay my bus fare I presented him with a Daimler double-six . . . and when I felt dull I let him drive it."[5] If Sayers is accurate, this is more like wish fulfillment than snobbery.

However, as Sayers grew older, she may well have seen some ambiguities in her (and her readers') attitudes toward Lord Peter The old joke about the opening of best-selling novels combining high life, sex, and religion ("'My God!' said the Duchess to the King, 'take your hand off my knee!'") may have held some truth, and Sayers, as an ex-advertisement writer, knew the devices. Hence (perhaps, in part) Mr. Montague Egg.

Equally qualified with "perhaps, in part," hence Miss Jane Eurydice Judkin. The title page of this story (reprinted here on page 79) shows that Sayers intended a series of stories under the title "The Situations of Judkin." If one may judge from "The Travelling Rug," Judkin is to tell a tale to an anonymous woman ("madam") about each interesting situation (read: *job*) that she has had.

That Sayers chose to tell a story in the voice of a maid, with some class dialect, with shifts between present and past tenses, shows a deliberate attempt to spread her range.[6] As suggested, it may also be a moral choice, to show that intelligence and basic goodness exist in servants as well as lords. Finally, a woman as detective would balance the masculinity of her two previous serial detectives. Sayers had written, in the introduction to *The*

Omnibus of Crime, that "the really brilliant woman detective has yet to be created."[7] At the time that she wrote that, Agatha Christie's first Miss Marple book had not yet appeared—*Murder at the Vicarage* (1930). Even with the competition of Miss Marple, Judkin would be a different type of woman. Perhaps (as the merest conjecture) the use of the first name *Jane* is an acknowledgement of Miss Marple's first appearance.[8]

Sayers often used her own background for details in her stories. Certainly, her parents had a household that included three maids. The chauffeur in the story may not have been from direct observation—her parents, at least in her early years, had a pony and a trap, and later her father drove a Model T Ford—but possibly some details came from Bill White, the father of her son—both White and Ludovic Maltravers were involved in transportation, White with riding motorcycles and (sometimes) selling automobiles, Maltravers as a chauffeur. Both were amorous men: "Bill was a physical type, not literary and not intellectual," writes Reynolds in her biography of Sayers; Maltravers propositions Judkin and is hardly a one-woman man. He shows no signs of literary interests. No doubt many differences existed between the men, but some hints may have come from White.[9]

When did Sayers create J.E. Judkin? The manuscript came to the Marion E. Wade Center in a purchase of papers from Sayers's son after her death, so there is no absolute *terminus ad quem* except for Sayers's death in 1957. But she stopped most work on detective fiction in 1937, as she began writing religious dramas. "The Haunted Policeman" (published in 1938) mentions the Wimseys' first son; "Talboys" (written in 1942) involves a Wimsey family of three boys. Except for Lord

Peter's reminiscence of Sherlock Holmes, broadcast in 1954, all of Sayers's detective fiction seems to have stopped sometime in the five-year period of 1937-1942, and that seems a likely time for the writing of "The Travelling Rug," to be left in manuscript as was "Talboys."[10]

If the date of the writing of "The Travelling Rug" is probable to a half-decade but not certain, still the story itself has a temporal setting of interest. Judkin says she worked for Miss Marsable for ten years, beginning at the age of fifteen. Miss Marsable died in 1922, so Judkin went to work for her in 1912. Fifteen years before that would put Judkin's birth in 1897, four years after Sayers's. (Since deaths and births do not occur just on January 1, all dates, except 1922, should have a possible variance of a year.)

Judkin indicates that after Miss Marsable's death she applied to the Registry for another job, and took the one with Mrs Fastowe, which is the story she tells. After that brief job, she had "a great many situations in a short time"—all the problems Sayers intended to write up. Then a gap seems to occur, for she appears to own her own house in the story. She points out items given her by her first two mistresses, which probably would not be out on display in a servant's quarters. Did she marry after the great number of jobs? Did something else occur? The story does not tell. But it does indicate that she is running a lodging house, for in the last paragraph, she refers to a gentleman who came to board with her. Judkin has made a leap from being a maid/cook to being in charge of (and perhaps owning) a boarding house.

Sayers has left both the "short time" of the situations and the relationship to the boarding house vague—probably with the intention of developing the details later. And exactly who is the woman to whom

Judkin speaks? The most likely answer is that she is checking out the boarding house for the purpose of placing a relative there. But other possibilities are open.

One final comment, on genre. The references above have called "The Travelling Rug" a mystery or a detective story. It is of what may be called the supernatural-explained type. For example, Sherlock Holmes in "The Adventure of the Sussex Vampire" investigates a situation in which a mother was discovered at the neck of her baby, with a bloody wound on the baby and blood on her lips. Holmes, as a rationalist, does not believe in vampires and finds a different explanation. In G.K. Chesterton's "The Ghost of Gideon Wise," a seeming ghost appears—that of a millionaire who was tossed (it is believed) over a "crumbling" cliff. The person who has confessed to the killing says, about his return to the area:

> "I could see the pale crests of spray appear and disappear as the great waves leapt up at the headland. Thrice I saw the momentary flash of foam in the moonlight and then I saw something inscrutable. The fourth flash of the silver foam seemed to be fixed in the sky. It did not fall; I waited with insane intensity for it to fall. I fancied I was mad: and that time had been for me mysteriously arrested or prolonged. Then I drew nearer, and then I think I screamed aloud. For that suspended spray, like unfallen snowflakes, had fitted together into a face and a figure, white as the shining leper in a legend and terrible as the fixed lightning."

Others subsequently see the same figure. In this story, Father Brown does not explain the seeming ghost is not a real ghost—that is made clear without his aid—but explains a different aspect of a crime. A third example may be offered: John Dickson Carr's "The Wrong Problem." Dr. Gideon Fell and Superintendent Hadley discuss a thirty-year-old series of murders with one of the persons originally involved. His step-father and the father of three other children was killed while sleeping in a summer house in the middle of a small lake; no one was seen going to the island that afternoon after the father went there by row boat. One of the other children said afterwards to the stepson, "We have either got to believe you killed him, or believe in the supernatural. Is the lake haunted? No, I think we may discard that." Two other deaths follow—the sister of the family and a swan—but the first one is that in which a supernatural possibility is briefly raised and denied.[11] Many other examples, both short stories and novels, could be cited. Often these stories are influenced by the Gothic mode: they take place in old, half-ruined castles or in isolated mansions; the weather tends to be stormy, with dark clouds and lightning flashes; the people involved may have Italian names and certainly have mysterious pasts and often laconic speech habits. In "The Wrong Problem," the "long gabled house" is a mile away from the nearest village. In "The Ghost of Gideon Wise," the ghost appears outside the millionaire's "bungalow on the coast" (the setting is the United States). "The Adventure of the Sussex Vampire" is laid in a house built "centuries ago"; the detective's visit takes place on "a dull, foggy November day." The walls of the main room have South American utensils and weapons for upper decorations; the "vampiress" is from Peru.

But Sayers's story, while it involves a poltergeist, does not use the supernatural Gothicism that is traditional from the late eighteenth century on. An early Gothic parallel closer to Sayers' work, but without a detective, appears in Ann Radcliffe's novels, which involve seemingly supernatural events that are eventually explained away—her best novel is usually considered to be *The Mysteries of Udolpho* (1794). By the seventh paragraph of Sayers's story, doubt is placed on the supernatural explanation. This tone seems to be, mostly, the effect of narrating the story through the common sense of Judkin. She is not one to wallow in her emotions.

Did Sayers intend all of Judkin's "situations" to involve the seemingly supernatural? In the first sentence of the story, Judkin announces she is a "specialist." Did she specialize in explaining away ghosts and other examples of the preternatural, or did she thwart various sorts of crimes, or did she more generally "solve" puzzles? How specialized was this specialist? Since Sayers did not write a second story and without the discovery of a comment in an unpublished letter, all one can do is guess.

One thing that a reader can be certain of, from "The Travelling Rug," is that the series would involve the puzzle plots of detective fiction's Golden Age, between the World Wars. Sayers, in her pronouncements on mystery fiction, strongly supported the presentation of all clues to the reader—letting him or her match wits with the detective as to their interpretation. Sometimes these plots are very artificial, and the story seems nothing but an ingenuous (if enjoyable) puzzle; other times the plot is a structure on which something else is found—an insight, a moral, a touch of meaningful characterization, perhaps just some delightful humor. The short story does not allow for quite as much leeway for such extras as do such novels as *The Nine Tailors* and *Gaudy Night*—but some pleasures it does offer. As does the story in this book.

Notes

[1] Sayers, ed., *The Omnibus of Crime* (1929), "Edgar Allan Poe: Evolution of the Detective" (sec. of the intro.). The British title of the anthology was *Great Short Stories of Detection, Mystery, and Horror* (1928). Sayers in a footnote indicates that the mystery was by both of the Coles, but her citation is of the first novel in their series, which was by G.D.H. Cole alone; perhaps a later reprint carried both their names. Wilson is listed as the detective in *The Brooklyn Murders* in the article on the Coles by Jeanne F. Bedell in *Twentieth-Century Crime and Mystery Writers*, ed. John M. Reilly (New York: St. Martin's Press, 1980).

[2] Sayers, "Edgar Allan Poe: Evolution of the Detective."

[3] A summary of Sayers's synopsis for this story is found in Barbara Reynolds's *Dorothy L. Sayers: Her Life and Soul* (New York: St. Martin's Press, 1993): 171-72. This biography has provided the details about Sayers's life used in this introduction. At least one discussion of Sayers's unpublished fragments about Lord Peter Wimsey has been published: Joe R. Christopher, "The Fragmentary Lord Peter," *Mythlore* 19.3/73 (Summer 1993): 23-26.

[4] Watson, *Snobbery with Violence: Crime Stories and Their Audience* (New York: St. Martin's Press, 1971): 148.

[5] Qtd. in Reynolds 230-31.

[6] A possibility exists (without evidence) that the story was written for broadcast, in which case the first-person narrative, as undertaken by an actress, would be quite effective. The Detection Club, of which Sayers became president after the death of Chesterton, wrote several books for broadcast. Note also Liza Cody's "Doing It under the Table" and "Chalk Mother" (both written in the first person, with a woman speaker; both broadcast over the BBC) in *"Lucky Dip" and Other Stories* (Norfolk, Virginia: Crippen and Landru, Publishers, 2003): 52-57, 102-107. (The failure in the parallel is that neither story by Cody involves a detective.) Of course, "The Young Lord Peter Consults Sherlock Holmes" is a first-person account by Lord Peter written by Sayers for broadcast.

[7] Sayers, "Edgar Allan Poe: Evolution of the Detective."

[8] Beth Russell of *Books—D & B Russell* has suggested a comparison with Patricia Wentworth's Miss Silver, rather than Christie's Miss Marple. Wentworth (pseudonym of Dora Amy Ellis Turnbull, 1878-1961) wrote a series of novels about Miss Silver, along with other novels: "The first book [about Miss Silver] … *Grey Mask* appeared in 1928, but only in the second, 1937—*The Case Is Closed*—did she appeared full-fledged. …Judson as [a] parlourmaid sleuth might be compared to … Miss Silver, a governess sleuth. …both earned their living[s] in other people's houses. [As is discussed later above, Miss Judson seems to have eventually gained some independence.] Miss Silver also earned an independence and could afford her own flat with a housekeeper. But she left her home from time to time to take a case, going to stay in a troubled household" (email of 12 February 2005).

[9] This parallel between White and Maltravers was suggested by Janet Brennan Croft (email of 29 March 2005).

[10] Barbara Reynolds has reported that she does not know the date of this manuscript (email of 12 March 2005).

[11] Sir Arthur Conan Doyle, "The Adventure of the Sussex Vampire" (1924) was collected in *The Case Book of Sherlock Holmes* (1927). G.K. Chesterton, "The Ghost of Gideon Wise" (1926) was collected in *The Incredulity of Father Brown* (1927). John Dickson

Carr, "The Wrong Problem" (1936) was collected in *Dr. Fell, Detective*, ed. Ellery Queen (1947); in *"The Third Bullet" and Other Stories* (1954); and in *Fell and Foul Play*, ed. Douglas G. Greene (1991). Sayers, in her introduction to *The Omnibus of Crime*, "Early History of Detective Fiction," mentions stories in which "the ghostly terror is invoked only to be dispelled"; her examples, without analysis, are Doyle's "The Adventure of the Speckled Band" and Chesterton's "The Hammer of God."

The Situations of Judkin

I.
THE
TRAVELLING RUG

By
Dorothy L. Sayers

Yes, madam, it's quite true I've had a great many situations[1] in a short time, but then you see, madam, I'm what you might call a specialist. I was just reading in the paper the other day that this was an age of specialisation, so I'm only moving with the times, as the saying goes.

I was all of ten years in my first place. That was with old Miss Marsable of Blathwick Hall. There was six indoor servants[2] kept in those days, and I started as kitchen-maid[3] when I was only fifteen. I

---

[1] Punning on 'situation' as a job and 'situation' as a set of circumstances. The title of the story is also a pun; a 'travelling rug' was used to keep passengers warm in a carriage or open car, but takes on another meaning in Sayers's plot.

[2] Servants who worked indoors, like cooks, butlers, and maids, outranked outdoor servants such as gardeners, coachmen, and stable hands. This is an establishment similar in size to that of the rectory at Bluntisham, where Sayers lived for ten years as a child. The rectory employed a cook, a manservant, three maids, a nurse (later replaced by a governess), a gardener, a laundry-maid, and a houseboy.

[3] A kitchen-maid assisted the cook.

was second house-maid[4] when the War[5] started, and then first house-maid, and then the mistress had to reduce the staff, owing to so much of her money being in foreign investments. Mr Chiddings, the butler,[6] was called up[7], too; so part of the house was closed and I stayed on as house-parlourmaid[8] with a girl under me.[9] Mr Chiddings taught me the silver and table work,[10] and of course I'd picked up a good bit about cooking when I was working in the kitchen; so when the crash came and Miss Marsable had to sell the place and take a little house in Rutherstone,[11] I

---

[4] A house-maid was the first out of bed in the morning, responsible for starting the fires, cleaning the house, mending, and a host of other duties.

[5] The First World War, 1914-1918.

[6] A butler was the chief manservant of a large establishment. Typically he would be responsible for the wine-cellar, maintaining discipline among the lower servants, supervising the serving of meals, answering the door, and paying accounts for non-housekeeping supplies.

[7] Drafted.

[8] A house-parlourmaid would be in charge of the drawing-room and other "public" rooms, help with the bedrooms, serve at meals, and assist in the kitchen.

[9] Probably a between maid, or "tweeny," who would do everything not the responsibility of the house-parlourmaid .

[10] *The Expert Waitress* by Anne Frances Springsteed (Harper and Brothers, 1912), covers serving at table in exhaustive detail and includes a chapter on caring for silver, brass, and other metal ware.

[11] Apparently a fictitious place.

was able to stay on with her as cook-general.[12]   She
was a proper lady, was Miss Marsable, one of the real
old-fashioned sort—you don't find many of them
nowadays.   A better mistress you couldn't wish for,
and I wouldn't have left her, not for any money.   But
she began to break up fast, poor dear, after we left
Blathwick, and she died in 1922. That's her silver tea-
service she left me; I'm very proud of that.   Real
Queen Anne,[13] and valuable, so they tell me—but of
course I wouldn't part with it, not if it was ever so.[14]

Well, I was twenty-five when Miss Marsable
passed away, and though I was very fond of her, of
course it was a very quiet situation towards the end.
So I told Miss Carrick up at the Registry[15] that I'd like
something with a little more life about it.   I had plenty
to pick and choose from; people couldn't get maids
then for love or money, but you see, I'd been trained
to *good* service, and I didn't want to go to any of these
new-rich as they call them, and the real gentlepeople
couldn't afford much in the way of wages.[16]

---

[12] A cook-general does both cooking and other
housework.

[13] Real Queen Anne silver would have been made 1702-
1714, characterized by graceful and unadorned lines.

[14] Judkin wouldn't sell the tea set even if it did prove to
be extremely valuable.

[15] A bureau that matched servants with situations. The
first one was established in London in 1749. In the early 1900s
registry agencies were regulated by the London City Council;
earlier, they had a doubtful reputation as fronts for prostitution.

[16] In post-war England, women willing to go into service
could afford to be fastidious in their choice of situation.   Young

Well, Miss Carrick had given me a list as long as your arm and was shutting up the book, when she began to laugh and said, casual-like: "If you want something lively, Jane, you might like to try Mrs Fastowe's. She's a real lady and she doesn't mind what she pays. She wants anything she can get — cook, house-parlourmaid, cook-general — whatever you like to call yourself. It's a pretty place, Mannering House[17] in Norfolk,[18] two miles from the town, but a car kept and good 'bus[19] service. And the chauffeur's[20] still there — at present."

"Oh!" I said. "And the rest of them left at short notice, is that it? What's the catch, Miss Carrick?"

"They've got a poltergeist,"[21] said Miss Carrick, and laughed again. Miss Carrick is very straight with

---

women were increasingly finding work in factories, as typists, telegraphers, nurses, and so on. Service was losing its attraction as a career path, in part because of long hours and social isolation.

[17] In 1920 Sayers met a film producer named Cyril Mannering. She wrote screen scenarios of Vincent Blasco Ibañez's *Blood and Sand* and several other novels for him, but nothing ever came of them.

[18] A county north-east of London, and the location of the ancestral home of the Wimsey family.

[19] Short for *omnibus*; *bus* is now the more common term.

[20] A chauffer was responsible not just for driving family members as needed but for the upkeep and cleanliness of their automobiles.

[21] A noisy, mischievous ghost. In the 1930s psychologist Nandor Fodor theorized that a supposed poltergeist's activities might be the unconscious psychokinetic manifestation of an adolescent's repressed hostility, anger, or sexual tension, and

her girls and always tells you if there's anything funny about a place.

Well, I didn't know then what a poltergeist was, but Miss Carrick explained that it was a kind of a ghost-affair that threw crockery and furniture about. "It's probably some silly person playing tricks," she said, "but the staff have got frightened and run away. Mrs Fastowe wants a good, sensible girl with a head on her shoulders. Do you fancy tackling the poltergeist? There's only two in the family—Mrs Fastowe and her invalid niece. She tells me she does any nursing that's needed herself, so you won't have to undertake that."

Well, I thought it over. By what Miss Carrick told me, the poltergeist did no harm to human beings, and though the household didn't sound exactly gay, it didn't sound dull, either. Besides, the money was good—and then, of course, there was the chauffeur. I mean, when you get to twenty-five, you don't want to miss anything.

☙

Sayers hints at this explanation for the events at Mannering in the character of Miss Brazey. Sayers also mentions poltergeists in *Strong Poison* and *Gaudy Night*.

Well, I got to the station all right, and there was the chauffeur to meet me; and believe me, madam, he was as per advertisement. I mean to say, if he had gone on the films he could have done the long, long kiss in the moonlit garden and given Clark Gable[22] and Ramon Novarro[23] a start and a beating. Features like a Greek god, as they say in the stories, and moving with the feline grace of a panther, only I never could abide them animals.

"You the young lady for Mannering House?" he says. And I said, "I'm the new housemaid." Mr Chiddings always taught us to be particular how we answered, ever since a temporary parlour-maid was shown in to the drawing-room[24] by mistake. "My name's Judkin," I went on, to make myself quite clear.

---

[22] Judkin compares the chauffeur to three film stars in the course of this story, all known for their swarthy good looks and legions of swooning female fans. But she could not have used Clark Gable (1901-1960) for an example in 1922 when the story was set, because he did not make his film debut till 1924 and didn't get screen credit until 1931. Gable is best known for *Gone With the Wind* (1939). Sayers also mentions Gable in *Busman's Honeymoon* (1937).

[23] Ramon Novarro (1899-1968) worked as an extra in silent films starting in 1917, and had his breakthrough role in *The Prisoner of Zenda* in 1922. He appeared in numerous films through the twenties and early thirties.

[24] Equivalent to the American living-room; a formal room where guests are received and afternoon tea is taken.

"I don't like the name," says he, kind of sparkling at me, like, and bending over me from the waist. "Haven't you got a prettier one? What comes before the Judkin?"

"*Miss* Judkin to you," says I—because panther or no panther, I thought he was taking things a bit for granted. Besides, at the Hall, the chauffeur was always expected to keep his proper distance.

"All right, *Miss* Judkin," says he, smiling away like a tooth-paste[25] advertisement—lovely white teeth he had, too—"you're a young lady of spirit, aren't you? I like 'em spirited. And you'll need to be, too, at our place."

And off he went to get my trunk.[26]

On the way to the house I asked him about the poltergeist.

"Oh, you've heard about that, have you?" says he. "And you're not afraid? There's lots of them would be. But I could see at once, you're not that sort."

"What's there to be afraid of?" said I. "It doesn't hurt anybody, does it?"

"Not so far," he said. "Not *hurt* anybody. No. It might play a few pranks in your bedroom, like

---

[25] Tooth-paste was first made available commercially in tubes in 1892.

[26] Servants kept their most personal belongings and important papers, like references, in a locked trunk. Often a servant didn't have room for her trunk in her room. Unscrupulous employers might hold a servant's trunk hostage to keep her from leaving.

pulling the clothes off the bed, but you wouldn't mind that, would you?"

"Seeing it's November," said I, "I should mind quite a lot."

"Perhaps it'll resist the temptation," says he, "though I don't know that I would, in its place."

He looked round in a way I didn't like. He had beautiful curly eye-lashes.

"You keep your eye on the road," I said, a bit short, like. "I'm much more afraid of a motor-smash than I am of poltergeists."

After that he told me a bit more. It seems the house had a reputation for being haunted before Mrs Fastowe came to live there. That was six months before, and the trouble had started almost at once, in a small way. Just little things at first, like doors opening unexpectedly, and the pots and pans being all put higgledy-piggledy in the night. After a time, the ghost seemed to get more confidence, and started to throw things about in broad daylight—quite heavy things. The servants didn't like it, and were always leaving, on some excuse or other. The final upset had happened about a week before, when a silver dish-cover[27] had come walking out of the pantry to meet the parlour-maid. She ran away, yelling, of course, fit to raise the roof, and just as she got into the kitchen, she met the cook coming out to see what all the noise was about. They were standing together in the

---

[27] Placed over a dish to keep food hot.

doorway when a big copper fish-kettle[28] came hopping off the high mantel-piece, right down where the cook had just been standing. That finished the two women. They went into hysterics, and my friend the chauffeur ran in from the garage, thinking the place was a-fire. By the time he'd sat them down and thrown water over them and run up to reassure Mrs Fastowe, who was sitting with her niece, the dish-cover had hung itself up on the hat-stand. The cook and the maid couldn't stand that, so they took themselves off next day without notice or wages, and the chauffeur (his name, or so he told me, was Ludovic Maltravers, a thing I didn't believe and my late mistress never would have permitted), he had to do all the work of the house for the next six days, with only a woman from the village coming in and leaving before it got dark.

"You've been here all the time, then," I said. "You must be terribly brave."

He liked that, of course. But he admitted he hadn't been there *all* the time, only the last four months. The man before him had left after words with Mrs Fastowe on account of water having been poured into his petrol[29] tank. They didn't realise about the poltergeist then, and he thought somebody had been playing a trick on him, while Mrs Fastowe thought he'd done it himself to get out of taking the car out in the rain and having it to clean afterwards.

---

[28] A large oval pan for boiling fish.
[29] Gasoline.

I hadn't been interviewed by Mrs Fastowe. She couldn't leave her niece—her having something wrong with her spine and not being able to get out of bed—and she was too thankful to get any sort of maid to bother very much what I was like, so she took me on my good reference. The first minute I saw her, I recognised that she was a lady, all right, but one of the helpless sort. I don't mean she couldn't see to things in the house and nurse her niece and so on; but she was a lady with no self-confidence. Been used to having her mind made up for her, I reckon, by Mr Fastowe, whoever he was when he was alive. She was fair and small and must have been pretty once in a fluffy kind of way. I could see she was dead frightened of the poltergeist and still more frightened that I should be frightened and leave.

She said she hoped I should be comfortable and work well and I said I would try to give satisfaction. And she asked what my name was. So I said, "My late mistress called me Judkin, madam." So she asked, what was my Christian name,[30] and I said, "Eurydice,[31] madam"—which was true, my Dad having read that name in a book just before I was

---

[30] First name.

[31] In Greek mythology, Eurydice was the wife of the musician Orpheus. When she died, he descended to the underworld to win her back from Hades. His music moved Hades to release Eurydice, on this condition that Orpheus not turn and look at her until they reached the upper world. But Orpheus was unable to keep from looking back, and lost her forever. Pronounced you-RID-eh-see.

christened and taken a fancy to it; but my mother had different ideas, so they made it Jane Eurydice. That rather took Mrs Fastowe aback, as you might say, because nobody could have a servant called Eurydice, and neither Ury nor Dissy sounds very well as a cut-short. So she said, "Oh, very well, Judkin." That showed me where I was with her (Miss Marsable would have said: "That won't do; you had better answer to Susan"), and it was one in the eye for Mr Ludovic Maltravers, since he couldn't get hold of my name through hearing me called by it.[32]

Mrs Fastowe showed me the house, which was all very nice, in an old-fashioned style, and told me what my work would be. The daily woman would come in to cook till Mrs Fastowe was suited,[33] and I was to do all the house and parlour work, except the brass, which was Maltravers's job. I thought Mrs Fastowe looked a bit nervous every time we passed anything like a big vase, and once when a door slammed she jumped right into the air; but the furniture didn't do anything out of the way, and

---

[32] Lower male and female servants were addressed by their first names only, and upper servants by their unadorned last names. A housekeeper or cook was entitled to the courtesy title of "Mrs". A butler would be addressed by his last name by his employer, but as "Mr" by the other servants. Judkin not only manages to keep her Christian name secret from Ludovic, she takes advantage of Mrs Fastowe's "fluffiness" and claims the privilege of an upper servant, whereas Miss Marsable would have countered this move by assigning her a suitable name.

[33] Until Mrs Fastowe was sure she would be satisfied with Judkin's cooking.

27

finally I was taken up to see the sick niece, Miss Brazey. She was on a kind of couch in a big, bright bedroom and looked thin and peaky and a bit peevish, to my thinking. She had sandy hair and very big, grey eyes, with a bright, intense look in them. She spoke nicely to me, and said she hoped I should be happy and settle down with them. And when I said, "Yes, miss; I'm sure I'll do my best," she looked very hard at me, as if she had her doubts. Mrs Fastowe didn't say anything to me about the poltergeist, and of course it wasn't my place to mention it; but Maltravers told me Miss Brazey knew nothing about it. So far, nothing had happened in her bedroom except a funny sort of perfume now and again, and they kept it from her, for fear of upsetting her. But I wasn't so sure that she didn't know anything. I know fright when I see it, and that girl was frightened, believe me. So then I went upstairs to change my dress and start on my work.

We got along pretty well that night. I suppose the poltergeist was kind of sizing me up and considering what he had best do with me, because, bar half a dozen tumblers[34] suddenly falling off the dresser[35] without a hand touching them, and the

---

[34] A tumbler was originally a drinking cup with a rounded bottom, so it could not be set down until it was empty. Now usually cylindrical or tapering to a flat bottom, without a handle.

[35] In British English, a cabinet or sideboard in the kitchen, though also applied to a chest of drawers in a bedroom as well.

gong[36] in the hall ringing very loud when Mrs Fastowe was at dinner and Ludovic helping me serve,[37] nothing out of the way happened. When the gong rang, I ran out quick, with a vegetable dish in my hand, but there wasn't anybody in the hall, and the gong-stick was hanging up quite quiet on its peg. Thank goodness the ghost left the dinner alone. The daily woman had got a casserole ready, and I did some potatoes to go with it and there was jam tarts to follow, which I thought I could have made lighter myself, if it had been left to me.

I locked my bedroom door that night—not on account of the ghost so much as of Ludovic, who slept in the house to protect us from whatever it was.[38] I was tired with my journey and slept sound; though I had an idea there were noises going on somewhere in the house. As well there might have been, because next morning we found all the kitchen pots and pans stacked up on the table in a kind of tower. The ghost must have put in a good hard bit of work: it took me over half an hour to get the mess straightened out and find the pan for the bacon and eggs.

---

[36] In households with servants, a gong was used to summon people to meals and announce the time to dress for dinner.

[37] In a smaller household, a coachman or chauffer might be asked to serve at table, but this was often a source of resentment for the servant.

[38] Like his ancestor the coachman, a chauffeur usually slept in an apartment over the garage.

I'd done all the breakfasts and taken them up by the time Mrs Poot arrived. She was a thin, bony sort of woman, with her hair all wisps and the most graveyard way of talking you ever heard. She came in on me when I was in the drawing-room, arranging a rug to cover over a big brown stain on the carpet near the fireplace.

"'Morning," she said. "You the new girl? Well, I only 'opes as you'll find the place agreeable."

"And why not?" says I. "The mistress seems a very nice lady."

"Ah!" said Mrs Poot. "*She's* all right. It's this 'ouse. But there! you'll find out soon enough. It's a 'ouse with a long memory. It ain't no use you trying to kiver up that there stain. It don't stay kivered."

"What do you mean?" says I.

"You can kiver up that there stain with that there rug," said Mrs Poot, "as many times as you like. But sooner or later it'll creep away off of it. There's things as can't be 'id."

"It's a nasty stain," says I, a bit short, like. "Why don't they send the carpet to the cleaners?"

"So they 'ave, dearie, so they 'ave. But the stain comes back. It came back in the old lady's time. It's a nasty stain, you're right there. Blood!" said Mrs Poot, leaning on her broom-handle and relishing the word as you might say. "Blood, dearie. You can't clean it out and you can't kiver it up. The pore senseless rug 'ull creep away off of it. You see if it don't."

"Whose blood?" said I. Because I've known plenty of stains came back after they been dry-cleaned, but they weren't blood.

"There was a man killed here once, dear," said Mrs Poot. "Murder, it was. Years ago. If you lift up the carpet, you'll find 'is life-blood in the boards. It soaks up through the carpet. If you was to put a new carpet down tomorrer, the stain 'ud come a-creeping up again afore you was many months older."

"Have they tried a new carpet?" I asked.

"No," said Mrs Poot, a bit grudgingly. "They ain't. It's the old carpet. But a new one would be just the same. Stains of murder won't never come out—everybody knows that."

"I don't believe a word of it," said I, patting the rug hard down into place.

"Ah!" said Mrs Poot. "You're young. You've a lot to learn yet. Well, I must be takin' me life in me 'and and gettin' on with me work. I don't so much mind the kittles[39] a-flyin' about—you can dodge kittles; but when it come to 'eavy wardrobes a-tryin' to squeedge you up agin the wall, forty shillin's a week don't 'ardly seem worth the risk."

Forty shillings a week! Did you ever hear the like, madam, for a country charwoman eight hours a day, with three meals given?[40] I made up my mind

---

[39] Kettles.

[40] Forty shillings = two pounds a week, or about £100 a year, with three meals a day provided (as well as, evidently, elevenses and tea). For comparison, in Brighton, a live-in cook made £40 a year in 1928. And in 1919, the Ministry of

then and there I could do the work myself, with Ludovic, and save the expense of Mrs Poot. I'd have given that myself, if I had it, to keep her ugly face out of my kitchen. She went off, shaking her head, to get herself her breakfast (and it's surprising what she could put away and stay so thin), and I went on with my dusting.

The drawing-room was one of the old-fashioned sort, with a lot of china about it, especially on the mantle-piece, which had one of them looking-glasses over it, all shelves; and there was a sight of vases and little figures on what-nots[41] and chiffoniers[42] all round the room. I made a good job of it though, getting up on a chair to do the chimney ornaments, which looked as if they hadn't been touched for months. The fire wasn't burning very well—the coal-merchant must have thought Mrs Fastowe a soft proposition—but I knelt down and had a good go at it with the bellows. After that, I had to go over some of the mantle piece again, but in the end I got it to go nice and cheerful. I turned back at the door before I left it to have a look at it and was thinking how pretty and bright it looked, when I saw something that give me quite a turn.

There was that queer stain showing again under the end of the hearthrug!

Reconstruction recommended seventeen shillings and sixpence a week for a single-handed cook with meals provided.

[41] A small piece of furniture with shelves for displaying ornaments and curiosities.

[42] A small cabinet, usually with drawers and a flat top.

Of course, it didn't take me a moment to tell myself that I must somehow have rucked the rug up while I was blowing the fire, and I soon had it straight. But I felt a bit of a fool, and I didn't say anything about it to Mrs Poot. But over our elevenses,[43] which she ate hearty of, I did get something out of her about the house and family. It seems the old lady that used to live there was Mrs Fastowe's great-aunt and she died and left her the house and an income to keep it up; but by the way the will was worded, if Mrs Fastowe left or let[44] the house, the money would pass away from her to Miss Brazey. Mr Fastowe had been a clerical[45] gentlemen, and left his widow very poor when he died; so she had to carry out the terms of the will, preferring the poltergeist, I suppose, to living dependent on her niece. Neither Mrs Poot nor Ludovic had a good word to say for Miss Brazey, and I made out she was one of these exacting invalids that nothing ever pleases. Not but what you couldn't help feeling sorry for her, lying there helpless, and having to be lifted from the bed to the sofa. They didn't rightly know what had caused the injury to her spine, only that she'd had a fall when she was at school; but the doctors said the trouble was due to the shock more than to the fall.

---

[43] Morning tea break, around eleven a.m.
[44] Rented out.
[45] A clergyman; a minister.

Mrs Fastowe had company that afternoon: the vicar[46] and his lady came to call. I took the tea up to the drawing-room, and I couldn't hardly believe my eyes when I saw that ugly old stain had come pushing out from under the rug again. I was so incensed with the stupid thing, I nearly made an excuse and set it to rights then and there; only I could see Mrs Fastowe looking at it in a nervous sort of way out of the corner of her eyes, as if she hoped it wouldn't be noticed. So I didn't draw attention to it. But I promised myself I'd take a hammer and tacks to it that night and see if the poltergeist could get over *that*.

My next job was to take up Miss Brazey's tray to her. She wasn't so well that day and was keeping in bed. The minute I got in, "Do you smell anything, Judkin?" she says to me. "Nothing, miss," I says, "only that joss-stick[47] you've been burning or whatever it is." "It's not a joss-stick," she says, "it's the perfume of the dead. It wasn't here an hour ago, but it comes every day. Aunt Angela pretends it comes in from the landing, but I know they mean it

---

[46] A minister in the Church of England. The word "vicar" comes from the Latin *vicarius*, a substitute; a vicar was hired and paid by the rector, who received the tithes of the parish, and the vicar did much of the actual work, such as preaching and ministering to the community. A vicar might even take this a step further and hire a chaplain or curate to do part of his work. Currently, all clergy stipends are paid centrally.

[47] Incense stick.

for me. Is there anything burning outside, Judkin? Tell me the truth, because Aunt Angela won't."

Well, I though I'd better mind my step, so I says: "I really couldn't say, miss; I'll go and see." But though you could smell it outside, it wasn't half so strong as it was in the room. So I searched every corner of the place, peeking into all the vases and looking in the fireplace and under the bed, and even, at the young lady's request, in the bed—for the scent seemed to hang all about her—though, naturally, you couldn't very well burn a thing like that under the bedclothes. "Don't you fret, miss," I said, "I'll find the thing, never fear, some day when you're up. It smells just like one of them little incense-cones you buy at the chemist's."[48]

"You'll never find it," she says, "it comes from the other side of the veil. How do you like this house, Judkin? It has a life of its own, and *I'm* afraid of it. Why doesn't Aunt Angela tell the truth? *I* can hear it muttering and walking in the night. I tell you, it's a house of the dead, and the dead are not happy. They can't rest. If the dead could rest, I should be at rest one day."

She had an awful queer look in her eyes, like as if she was scared out of her wits—and just as I was going to say something, there comes a most awful banging and clattering like fifty thousand million tin trays falling through a greenhouse. "Oh, my God!" calls out Miss Brazey, "what's that?" "Sounds like

[48] Drugstore or pharmacy.

something falling down, miss," says I, taking it calm, like, though I could hear somebody screaming like anything down below. "I'll go and pick it up," I says, and I walks out and looks over the banisters. What I see made me run downstairs in a hurry. There was Mrs Vicar standing in the hall, shrieking her head off, and the reverend gentleman holding her up, and Mrs Fastowe wringing her hands and Ludovic running in from the garden with his face like a sheet and string he'd been marking out a new bed with trailing behind him and Mrs Poot after him—her having run out the back way yelling fire and blue murder—and there was a huge great brass pot of that Indian sort, (Benares ware[49] they call it, don't they?) that stood in the top landing with an aspidistra[50] in it, laying in the hall and the great mirror opposite the front door all smashed into stars and stripes where the flower pot had hit it.

"Oh, dear me," says I to myself, "somebody's going to have bad luck, and I hope it's the poltergeist."

So Mrs Vicar points her finger at me, all shaking, and squeaks out: "Did you do that?"

Well, I thought maybe it would make matters pleasanter if I took the blame, so I says: "Yes, madam,

---

[49] Decorated brassware made in Benares, now Varenesi, India. May be gilded.

[50] An evergreen, broad leaved plant that thrives in poor indoor conditions, sometimes a symbol of Victorian middle-class respectability (see George Orwell's *Keep the Aspidistra Flying*, 1936).

and I'm sure I'm very sorry. How it came to slip out of my hand I can't think and I'm sure it's a mercy there was nobody hurt." And I picks up the pot, as was all dinted in, and I says to Mrs Fastowe, "Mind the broken glass, madam," I says. "I'll just fetch my dust-pan and brush and have it all swept up in a minute." The mistress looked very hard and queer at me, but she plucked her courage up (and that showed she was a real lady after all) and she says: "It was most careless of you, Judkin. You might easily have killed somebody." And as I went off for the dust-pan, I heard her apologising to the lady and gentleman.

So I swept up the bits and then nipped upstairs to tell Miss Brazey it was only Mrs Poot had an accident with the Benares pot (thinking Mrs P. might take her share of the trouble, and not mentioning the mirror); and when I came down again, the guests were just leaving and I showed them out. So Mrs Fastowe says to me: "Did you really do that, Judkin?" And I said, "No, madam, but I thought it best to say I did." And she said, "Quite right, Judkin. That was sensible of you." And she never said another word, but went straight up to Miss Brazey, and I went into the drawing-room and stared at that stupid rug and the stain on the carpet.

It wasn't what I should have called a suitable rug for the room. It was a lot newer than the carpet and had one of those kind of up-to-date patterns all in straight lines, while the carpet was all cabbage-roses.[51]

---

[51] A double red rose with a large round flower.

I guessed it had been got to cover up the stain in place of a shorter one. I had a good look at that rug, front and back, and then I decided I wouldn't tack it down, but give it one more chance to behave itself. Only this time I turned it round with its front edge against the fender.[52] It looked a bit funny that way, because the pattern was a kind of sunrise affair with rays shooting out from a round thing at one side; and of course I could see it was meant to look as if the rays were coming out from the fireplace, like. All the same, I turned it round. I knew, if they noticed anything, they'd just think it was the new maid being stupid. After that, I went up to the top landing and looked at the place the Benares pot had fallen from. It had used to stand on one of those mahogany[53] pedestals, close to the banisters, and the top of the pedestal came just above the banister-rail. A silly place, I thought, to stand a thing like that. Anyone knocking against it might have tipped it over—only, of course, there hadn't been anybody there. I leant over and looked down into the hall to see where the thing had gone over—and then I jumped right up in the air. Something touched me on the back of the neck—just like a cold, icy finger it was. I just stopped myself letting out a yell. I was glad, next minute, I hadn't been such a fool. It was only the landing window

---

[52] A metal frame placed in front of the fire, to keep coals from rolling out into the room.

[53] A reddish-brown wood with a straight grain and even texture.

open and a gust of rain blowing in; but it just showed me I was getting jumpy.

"Now then, Jane Eurydice," I said to myself, "pull yourself together, my girl." And I shut the window and went down to the kitchen.

Well, it seems as if the ghost had made up its mind that evening I was the kind of person that needed strong measures. If I was to tell you the way that house behaved I should never have done. First it was the gong ringing, on and off, on and off, and then it was doors banging and things tumbling down and once something went off with a great bang in the garden. The poor mistress gave up all pretence that things were as they should be. She and I and Ludovic kept running round the place with the poker, and every time, when we got to where the noise had come from, something would start off in a different part of the house. Chronic,[54] it was. What with the noises and the running about, Miss Brazey started to ring her bell like mad and said she was too frightened to be left alone. So then Mrs Fastowe went to sit with her, and Ludovic and I went round the place by ourselves; which I didn't like, because it's bad enough to be hunting for ghosts in the middle of the night without somebody trying to kiss you every time he got you into a dark corner. And then, just as the clock struck midnight, every light in the house went out, and I had to go down with Ludovic and hold the

---

[54] Unpleasant, objectionable, unfair.

torch[55] while he replaced the main fuse. I scratched his face, though, and he wasn't too pleased about it. That was the last of the disturbances, and we all went to bed.

I did a good bit of thinking that night. I don't know why it was, but I couldn't believe in a ghost that would take the main fuse out of its box and put in a bit of fine wire in its place. It seemed to me, a real ghost ought to be able to work a blow-out without making use of a screw-driver. Ludovic hadn't drawn attention to the fuse-wire—I suppose he thought, being a woman, I should be too stupid to understand; but when Miss Marsable had her little house I'd learnt all about fuses. I could even connect up a new lamp or mend the switch if I was put to it. I'm neat with my hands, Dad having been a joiner and cabinet-maker.[56] In fact, I'd have had my suspicions of Ludovic, only I couldn't see why he should want to play at ghosts. And besides, he couldn't have rung the gong in the hall while he was helping me in the dining-room. But next day I came down with my mind made up to do a bit of house-cleaning. I'm sure the place needed it. I was up at five and starting to work in the kitchen, and the dust on the top of the dresser was a thing you wouldn't hardly believe. There were one or two holes in the walls, too, but I got a bit of putty from Ludovic's tool-shed and stopped them up; and while I was hunting

---

[55] Flashlight.
[56] Fine woodworker.

40

about there I found a box full of that very fine catgut[57] that Miss Marsable's great-nephew, Mr John, used to use for making his trout-casts. I cut off a good long piece of that and put it in my pocket, thinking it might come in handy for an idea I had in my mind. I'd done all the kitchen and scullery[58] thoroughly by breakfast time, with the help of Serafina,[59] the black cat. An intelligent, sensible creature she was, and must have seen a lot, going about at night the way she did. Her and me was great friends. I had her in with me while I scrubbed out the outside larder,[60] and she was as good as gold, sitting up on the shelf like a little image[61] and never offering to touch the milk nor nothing. I was singing away at my work, when I heard Mrs Poot come along the passage and go into the house, leaving the scullery door open behind her. She hadn't been there five minutes when she let out a big scream, and when I came in to see what was up,

---

[57] A tough cord usually made from sheep intestines.

[58] A room for washing dishes and other heavy cleaning. Not usually found in modern buildings.

[59] Saint Serafina, of San Gimignano in Tuscany, was paralyzed for six years and had to be lifted and moved by others, much like Miss Brazey. Her feast day is March 12, and she is the patron saint of the handicapped.

[60] In the days before refrigeration, a dry and well-ventilated outdoor larder in a shady place was the best place to keep meat and dairy products fresh. Mrs Fastowe would not have had a refrigerator in 1922, since they were not introduced to England from America until about 1924. Apparently she did not have an ice-box, either.

[61] Statue.

there was the big meat-safe[62] strolling round the kitchen floor. Funny it did look. I must say, I couldn't hardly help laughing, but I picks up the safe and shows her Serafina sitting inside.

"Thought it was the ghost, did you, Mrs Poot?" says I. "Well, I put one over on you there." And I took the meat-safe back to the larder, leaving her exclaiming and holding her hand to her heart. Ludovic came in then and I heard her telling him all about it. He wasn't best pleased, Ludovic wasn't, and came out and told me I didn't ought to play them tricks; I might have been the death of the poor woman. "All right, all right," I says, "Rudolph Valentino,[63] keep your hair on. Mrs Poot's seen worse than a poor cat in a meat-safe." And I sloshes a pail of water over the floor, so he had to skip out of the way quick to save those nasty yellow boots of his. And if Miss Marsable had seen her chauffeur in boots like that, she'd have had him on the mat[64] good and proper.

---

[62] A meat-safe is usually a ventilated cupboard for storing meat, but in this case is more likely to be a dome of wire mesh or perforated metal placed over food to protect it from flies and other insects. Sayers was still using a meat-safe in her kitchen shortly after her marriage in 1926.

[63] Rudolph Valentino (1895-1926) was the archetypal hot-tempered Latin lover on screen and off. His career began in the early days of silent film, and when he died in 1926 there were scenes of mass hysteria. He is best known for *The Sheik* (1921).

[64] Originally a British military term; Miss Marsable would have called him in for a reprimand.

Well, I'd got an appetite for breakfast by that time, and it didn't worry me that I didn't seem to be what you might call popular in the kitchen. So after I'd done myself proud on the eggs and bacon and taken up the trays, I set Mrs Poot to turn out the hall and landing and went to dust the drawing-room. And there wasn't no stain showing on the carpet this time, neither. Not but what the hearthrug had been walking all right; only this time it had walked in the other direction, so to speak, and was making for the chiffonier, so that the stain come right under the middle of it instead of at one end. Well, that was all right, so far, and the next thing I wanted to do was to look into that funny smell in Miss Brazey's room. Only it was difficult to have a thorough turn-out there, owing to her being always in her room and not to be disturbed.

I must say, if any girl wants to do pretty much as she likes and no questions asked, she can't do much better than take a situation with a poltergeist. Anything at all that went wrong at Mannering House was put down to the spook. When half a leg of mutton disappeared from the larder, that was the spook—though I happened to call in on Mrs Poot that same evening to ask about a bit of laundry wanted doing, and they was having cold mutton for supper. And when the soup was burnt, that was the spook too. And so, when one evening there was a big can of motor oil found in Miss Brazey's bed with the cap half-unscrewed and all the oil leaking into the mattress, that was put down to the spook without any hesitation. I told Mrs Fastowe there was no can there when I went to make the bed in the morning, and no more there was, for I didn't put it in till I brought up the hot-water bottles[65] at dinner-time. I found the can there when I went up to turn down the bed and if you'll believe me, I was so misfortunate, pulling the clothes down to see what the trouble was, that I pulled the bottle out and the oil went all over the floor and pretty well ruined a pretty rug that lay by the bed. Of course, Miss Brazey couldn't sleep there with the bed all oily, so we had to make up the bed in the spare room and get Ludovic Maltravers to help carry her in. Such a to-do there was. Miss Brazey had hysterics, screaming out that she knew the house was haunted and poor Mrs Fastowe had to tell her the whole story. I was really sorry to have made such a lot of trouble, but I wanted to get that bedroom clear. Ludovic came along when I was stripping the mattress off and wanted to help, but I said I could manage by myself, thank him kindly; and I turned him out and came out myself and locked the door and put the key in my pocket.

The can of oil had passed off so nicely, being all put down to the poltergeist, I thought I'd have another try at producing what the spirit-rapping gentry[66] call a phenomena or two. That morning

---

[65] A housemaid would be responsible for warming the beds in the evening.

[66] Spiritualism, séances, and mediums who promised communication with the dead became a craze in Victorian England, and even Sir Arthur Conan Doyle was taken in by

when I was doing my kitchen I'd picked out a big old copper preserving-pan[67] that stood on a high shelf near the kitchen window. I rolled it close to the edge, where a touch would send it over, and I got Ludovic's bit of fishing-tackle and slipped it through one handle and ran both ends out through a chink at the top of the window and let them hang down by the wall near the rain-water butt.[68] You couldn't notice anything either inside or outside, the gut being so fine; and now I thought would be a good time to try it. So I waited till Ludovic had settled himself down in his chair by the fire and put in one of his everlasting cigarettes, and said something about getting a jug of rain water to wash my hair with. He didn't pay much attention; so I went out and found the two ends of the gut and pulled hard. My aunt! you never heard such a row! The pan came down beautiful and bounced off the edge of the flour-bin, and Ludovic jumped as if he'd a-been shot. I was that excited, I almost forgot to let go one end of the gut and haul it out, and if he'd been quick he'd have seen it go; but he stood there

---

them. Judkin uses "gentry" in a playful or mocking sense here, but the well-off seemed particularly gullible about the supernatural. In mid-1800s, for example, America sisters Margaret and Kate Fox learned to crack their big toe joints at will and created a sensation with their demonstrations of "spirit-rapping" and communication with the other world.

[67] A large pan for slow cooking of jams and jellies.

[68] A barrel for collecting rain-water from a downspout or gutter. Rain-water was thought to be particularly "soft" and good for washing hair.

like a stuck pig, and the line come away beautiful and I bundled it up and pushed the lot into the water-butt before I come running in to ask what the noise was. "My God!" says he, "did you hear that?" "Of course I heard it," says I, "not being deaf. What's the matter with you? It's only the poltergeist—you ought to be used to that by this time." Well, just then the drawing-room bell rang and I went along to see what the mistress wanted. It seemed Miss Brazey had asked her aunt to make her a brandy flip[69] and Mrs Fastowe was coming out to the kitchen with the decanter when she suddenly came over faint, hearing the clatter, and had to go back and sit down. "You do look white, madam," I said, and so she did, poor soul. "Take a little glass yourself, madam," I said, "I'll make the flip in a minute and run up with it. I used to make brandy flips for my late mistress," I said, "and you can trust me, madam." So back I went to the kitchen and whipped up the egg and put the sugar and brandy to it and started upstairs. And just as I got to the turn of the landing, who should I see but my lord Ludovic, coming out of the spare room where we'd put Miss Brazey. "Well," I said to myself,

---

[69] A brandy flip would be considered a nourishing drink for an invalid, and a good early morning or bedtime drink. It consists of an egg, one teaspoon powdered sugar, 1 ½ ounce brandy, and 2 teaspoons sweet cream (if desired). Shake well with cracked ice and strain into a five-ounce glass. Serve with grated nutmeg on top. There is also a hot brandy flip, but as Judkin doesn't say anything about heating up milk, we can probably assume Miss Brazey's drink was served cold.

"if that don't beat the band! And what are you doing up here?" I says to him. "Oh," he says, "I just went up to tell the young lady not to be frightened, it was only a saucepan fallen down in the scullery." "Saucepan to you," I says. "Miss Brazey couldn't hear nothing this side of the house. You keep your saucepans till they're wanted, and your sauce too," I says. And I took the flip in, and Miss Brazey said nothing to me nor me to her, not being my place, but like the monkey I thought all the more.[70] Especially, when, coming out again[71] with the tray, there's his nibs[72] trying the door of Miss Brazey's own bedroom. "Well, and what next?" I said to him. "Miss Brazey wants something out of her room," says he, bold as brass. "Well," I says, "I'm the proper person to fetch it, not you. What is it?" "It's a blue silk scarf," says he. "All right," I says, "I'll get it. You buzz off, my lad," I says, seeing him still hanging about.

---

[70] I have not been able to trace this reference. Possibly Sayers refers to the Rudyard Kipling poem, "The Legend of Evil," in which monkeys do not speak because they are afraid they will be put to work, like humans. A similar reference occurs in Kenneth Grahame's short story "Lusisti Salis": "Monkeys, who very sensibly refrain from speech, lest they should be set to earn their livings."

[71] There are two drafts of the "searching the room" section of the manuscript. The second draft is given here, and the first draft at the end of this transcription. The reproduction of the handwritten manuscript starting on page 79 shows them in the order written.

[72] A mock title used ironically, implying the person referred to has an inflated sense of self-importance.

"Anybody'd think you'd done a murder in there and was looking for a chance to wipe off the finger-prints."[73]   That shut him up proper, and I thinks: "He's left something there he don't want me to find, and I'd like to know how that came about."   So I went in and got the scarf, and took it to Miss Brazey, who said, "Thank-you, Judkin," without looking at me; and then back I went and stripped that bed down to the bones.   And when I'd got the mattress and underlay off I got a torch and had a good look underneath.   And there on the rim of the bed-frame under the spring, if you'll believe me, I found a little tin tray no bigger than a match-box and standing in it a little pyramid of ash, like the ghost of one of those incense-cones.   It seemed a funny thing to me how anybody could put it there and light it, without Miss Brazey noticing.   You couldn't get at it by lifting the mattress, on account of the spring; you'd have to crawl under the bed.

Well, that made me think a bit, I can tell you, and I wondered if I'd find any more funny things about the room.   I went all over it with a tooth-comb,[74] as they say, and to cut a long story short, I shoved my hand down at the back of Miss Brazey's couch, between the head-rest and the seat, and out came an awful queer thing.   It was just a round ball of wood

---

[73] The first fingerprint files in London were established in 1901.

[74] A fine-toothed comb.

tied on the end of a long black elastic[75] – for all the world like one of those yo-yos the boys used to play with a few years ago. I put that back where I found it and left the little mound of ash just where it was, and said nothing to nobody; only when I went downstairs again, I left the key of the room conspicuous-like, on the dresser.

᪘

---

[75] An elastic cord or string, usually woven with India-rubber.

The ghost was pretty active about the house that night—spiteful he was, too, filling the saucepans with soot and putting the salt in the castor-sugar[76]—and when I started in to do the bedroom in the morning, the key was where I'd left it, but the little cone of ash and the yo-yo were napoo,[77] as they used to say in the war.

Of course, Miss Brazey wanted to get back into her own room; so I put on a mattress out of one of the other rooms, and sent the soiled one to the cleaner's with the bedside rug. And I brought up the drawing-room rug and put it by the bed. I don't know what Mrs Fastowe thought about that. She didn't make any remark, and after all, the drawing-room could do quite well without a hearthrug for a few days. The only thing I was afraid of was that the proper rug might come back before the ghost did the gong trick again; but I was lucky. It wasn't more than two days later, when I was waiting at dinner, when the gong went off, "Boom!" I was carrying the joint in at the moment and I just shoved the dish into Ludovic's hands and said, "Hold that!" and I ran upstairs like a

---

[76] Castor sugar is more finely ground than American granulated sugar, but not as fine as powdered sugar. Generally for table use, in drinks or on cereal.

[77] Napoo, adjective or interjection, meaning finished, gone, done for. World War I slang; an Anglicization of the French phrase *il n'y en a plus*, 'there is no more'.

lamplighter[78] as they say, though I never seen one of them do such a thing. I bust into Miss Brazey's room without knocking. She was lying in her bed reading a book, and she looked awful scared to see me come rushing in that way. "What's the matter, Judkin?" she says. And I took a look at the rug by the bedside and I says, "I see you've been out of bed, Miss. I'm sure I'm very happy to congratulate you on your recovery. The mistress *will* be pleased." "Out of bed, Judkin?" says she, "You must be out of your mind." "No, miss," I said. "Just you look at that rug. When I brought your tray up, I set the edge of it straight with that square on the carpet, and now it's crept down half a foot. That rug always walks when it's trodden on, but it can't walk of itself; and there's been nobody up here since we started dinner, I can take my oath of that." And then I looks round, and there's the mistress standing at the door, and dreadful white she was.

"What's all this, Judkin?" says Mrs Fastowe. And I says, "I'm happy to say, madam, as the young lady has recovered the use of her limbs." And with that I went out and left them to it, only I called Ludovic and said, "Madam wants you up in Miss Brazey's room." And when he got up there, I hears the young lady call out very pitiful, "Oh, Ludovic, darling!"

---

[78] A lamplighter lit the street lamps, and supposedly ran his rounds or ran up his ladder with great rapidity.

And thinking it was a pity the joint should get cold, I pops it back in a slow oven[79] and sits down to a bit of sewing.

Well, madam, it was all cleared up quite comfortable. It seems Miss Brazey's trouble was of a hysterical sort,[80] after all. She hadn't been much thought of at home or at school, and when she had her fall and was laid up, she enjoyed being the centre of attention. So after that she went on play-acting, and presently after they came to Mannering House, she got the idea of playing tricks, just to give herself importance, like. Just little things at first; but when Ludovic came, he caught her at it and threatened to tell the mistress. Only then he got the idea of bettering himself, and he made love to the poor girl, slipping in of an evening when the mistress was out of the way; and the plot they made up between them was to frighten Mrs Fastowe out of the house, so that the money should come to Miss Brazey, and then he was to marry the young lady and hang his hat up in Mannering House for keeps. What with him hauling the heavy stuff about with his fishing-tackle and his ropes through the windows, and what with her creeping out when he was in the dining-room, and banging the gong with her yo-yo affair let down over

---

[79] A slow oven is about 300° Fahrenheit or 150° Celsius. Old cookbooks often specify a slow, moderate, or hot oven rather than giving specific temperatures.

[80] A psychosomatic illness, with no apparent physical cause. At one point almost any illness suffered by a woman was ascribed to hysteria.

the banisters, they worked the tricks easy enough. And that old fool Mrs Poot helped them along unconscious like, with her silly tales about blood and murders—which the stain on the carpet turned out to be nothing worse than some kind of liqueur, and there never was no murder in the house at all, the gentleman having died in a fit.

It seems there was sad trouble with Miss Brazey over Ludovic. Really attached to him and his eyelashes and his Greek nose she was, poor girl—and, of course, the minute it was all found out and there was no money with her, he backed out of it, not caring a snap of his fingers for her. She was really and truly ill after that, and Mrs Fastowe took her abroad to get over the shock. When they came back to the house, she wanted me to stay on as head parlour-maid; but I made up my mind as the situation wouldn't suit me. Miss Brazey had took a kind of dislike to me, and it wouldn't have been comfortable.

Mrs Fastowe was very kind indeed—she was a nice lady—and behaved very generous. She gave me a present of the drawing-room rug, too; that's it over there. If you step on it, madam, you'll see that it moves under your weight. I showed it to a scientific gentleman who came to board with me.[81] He was ever so interested—said it was due to the hairs on its

---

[81] It was a common ambition of upper servants to save enough to open their own boarding house. The well-known five-star London hotel, Claridge's, originated as a boarding house run by a retired butler and his housekeeper wife.

underneath being stiff and all lying in the same way, so that they hooked into the pile of the carpet. Snakes, he said, has their scales set that way, and that's how they get along;[82] but I never could abide them things.

$$\mathcal{SO}\,\mathcal{CR}$$

---

[82] Species of snakes which move in rectilinear progression, or "inchworm" fashion, use their ventral muscles to raise the squared-off back edges of special scales on their belly enough to grip the ground and move them forward.

SEARCHING THE ROOM, FIRST DRAFT:

…with the tray, there's his nibs trying the door of Miss Brazey's own bedroom. "Well and what next?" I said to him. "Oh," says he, "I thought I might have dropped my cigarette lighter out of my pocket when I went in to help with Miss Brazey." "Oh, indeed?" says I; "well, I'll have to hunt for it when I turns the room out to-morrow." "Be a sport, Judy," he says (that being the name he'd made up for me out of Judkin), "let's go in and have a look now." "What's the hurry?" says I. "Won't a box of matches do for you for to-night? Anybody'd think you'd done a murder in there and left your finger-prints about." That shut him up all right. "Well," I thinks to myself, "he's left something there he don't want me to find, and he went in to ask Miss Brazey if she had another key." And then it came over me, there might be another key in the house to fit that lock after all, and I'd better have a look round before anybody else got in. So when Ludovic had gone off downstairs, I got a torch and went into the room to see what I could find. And it didn't take me so long, neither; because, when I'd got the soiled mattress and the underlay stripped off the bed, there, if you'll believe me, was a little china ash-tray perched in one of the angle irons beneath the springs, and a little pyramid of ash in it, like a burnt-out ghost of one of those incense cones. You couldn't possibly see it when the bed was made up, not even if you crawled underneath; and I know it hadn't been there when I made the bed in the morning. It seemed funny to me how anybody could have put it there without Miss Brazey noticing. I didn't touch it; only when I went downstairs I left the bedroom key, careless like, on the dresser.

Some resources consulted for annotations:

Bartlett, John. *Familiar Quotations*. Fifteenth edition.
     Boston: Little, Brown, 1980.
Beeton, Isabella. *The Book of Household Management*.
     Originally published 1861. New York: Farrar
     Straus Giroux, 1969.
Clarke, Stephan P. *The Lord Peter Wimsey Companion*.
     Second edition. Hurstpierspoint, Dorothy L. Sayers
     Society, 1985.
Cotton, Leo, ed. *The Old Mr. Boston De Luxe Official
     Bartender's Guide*. Boston: Mr. Boston, 1964.
Ebery, Mark, and Brian Preston. *Domestic Service in Late
     Victorian and Edwardian England, 1871-1914*.
     University of Reading, 1976.
Grote, David. *British English for American Readers*.
     Westport: Greenwood Press, 1992.
Horn, Pamela. *The Rise and Fall of the Victorian Servant*.
     Glouchestershire: Sutton Publishing, 1990.
Huggett, Frank E. *Life Below Stairs: Domestic Servants in
     England from Victorian Times*. New York: Scribner,
     1977.
Internet Movie Database. 30 June 2005. www.imdb.com.
Oxford English Dictionary Online. Oxford University Press.
     30 June 2005. www.dictionary.oed.com.

Partridge, Eric. *A Concise Dictionary of Slang and Unconventional English*. Abridged by Paul Beale. New York: Macmillan, 1989.

Reynolds, Barbara. *Dorothy L. Sayers: Her Life and Soul*. New York: St. Martin's, 1993.

Schur, Norman W. *British English, A to Zed*. New York: Facts on File, 1987.

Springsteed, Anne Frances. *The Expert Waitress*. New edition, revised and enlarged. New York: Harper and Brothers, 1912.

Turner, E.S. *What the Butler Saw: Two Hundred and Fifty Years of the Servant Problem*. New York: St. Martin's Press, 1963.

A Checklist of Dorothy L. Sayers's Short Mystery Fiction

Compiled by Joe R. Christopher

This list of stories has been organized by annotating three series first—two of serial detectives, one of serial crime stories—followed by the miscellaneous mystery short stories. Between these series and the miscellaneous stories is placed "The Travelling Rug." Sayers wrote at least one story, before her mystery writing days, that is not listed below ("Who Calls the Tune?," *The Blue Moon* [private journal of a group of Sayers's friends] 1.1 [1917]; the manuscript of that story is available at the Wade Center, Wheaton College, Wheaton, Illinois). She also published four retellings of Bible stories in 1955. Books and stories have been dated by first publication, but further details have been omitted. For Sayers, the basic bibliography is Colleen B. Gilbert's *A Bibliography of the Works of Dorothy L. Sayers* (Hamden, Connecticut: Archon Books, 1978); and it will provide all omitted publication material about her stories and books up to approximately its date of publication. Undated stories have not as yet had their journal publications discovered, if they appeared anywhere previous to book publication.

Lord Peter Wimsey

The first twelve stories below appeared in the present order in *Lord Peter Views the Body* (1928) and in *Lord Peter: A Collection of All the Lord Peter Wimsey Stories,* comp. James Sandoe (1972). The next four stories appeared in this order in *Hangman's Holiday* (1933) and in *Lord Peter.* The next two stories appeared in this order in *"In the Teeth of Evidence" and Other Stories* (1939) and in *Lord Peter.* The following two stories first appeared in this order in *Lord Peter,* and the subsequent story first appeared in the second edition of *Lord Peter* (1972 also). The final "story" — actually an anecdotal radio speech as by Lord Peter — was first published in *Sayers on Holmes: Essays and Fiction on Sherlock Holmes by Dorothy L. Sayers* (2001).

"The Abominable History of the Man with Copper Fingers"

In what is usually called a "club story" — a group of men talking in a private club in London — an American actor tells of his experiences with a sculptor and his wife in New York, and Wimsey (who also had been in New York) finishes the story. This is one of the two stories rejected for publication by *Pearson's* magazine because it was too gruesome.

"The Entertaining Episode of the Article in Question" (1925)

Wimsey, in a queue in a train station in Paris, changes his plans and proceeds directly back to London, there (in three days) contacting the

Dowager Duchess of Medway and getting himself invited to her granddaughter's wedding. The crime itself is committed near the end of the story. The titular "article" requires a knowledge of French.

"The Fascinating Problem of Uncle Meleager's Will" (1925)

Lady Mary asks her brother to help Hannah Marryat discover her uncle's final will. A crossword puzzle—then a new rage—figures in the tale, with both clues and square provided. (The solution to the crossword, with some explanation of the clues, appears at the end of *Lord Peter Views the Body* and after "The Adventurous Exploit of the Cave of Ali Baba" in *Lord Peter*.) To tie the story together thematically, Bunter is involved in working crossword puzzles also.

"The Fantastic Horror of the Cat in the Bag"

The story opens with two motorcyclists racing up the Great North Road. The mystery involves the contents of a bag that one of them has tied to his motorcycle: he insists the other motorcyclist lost the bag; the other denies it. Lord Peter shows up in a car, seeking a similar bag with jewelry in it—but this bag turns out to not be it. The titular "cat" is not literally a cat.

"The Unprincipled Affair of the Practical Joker" (1926)

The wife of a diamond merchant contacts Lord Peter to ask him to regain some items stolen from her. The problem is not who took the items but the means of regaining them. Wimsey gives himself two weeks to achieve the goal.

"The Undignified Melodrama of the Bone of Contention"

Wimsey, visiting a friend in Essex, sees a luminous coach with four horses—the horses and the driver are headless. The story also involves a disreputable, dead local squire and his lost will. The coach is believed by the folk to appear when a squire dies—and to bode ill for those who see it.

"The Vindictive Story of the Footsteps that Ran"

While Lord Peter and Bunter are with a doctor in his ground-floor flat in Bloomsbury one Sunday morning, a woman is stabbed in the flat above. This story is dated as to year, 1921—perhaps the summer then was especially hot, as it is in the tale. The fiction emphasizes the unconscious mind catching details that the conscious mind is not completely aware of; this causes the meaning of the titular footsteps to be not given as a clue, but only realized to be meaningful later. This contrasts with the clue of the pattern of the footsteps heard by Father Brown in G. K. Chesterton's story "The Queer Feet" (1910; collected in *The Innocence of Father Brown*, 1911). This was the second story rejected by *Pearson's* as too gruesome.

"The Bibulous Business of a Matter of Taste"

Two Lord Peters and a cousin of Lord Peter, Death Bredon, all arrive at the Comte de Rueil's chateau on the same day, at approximately the same time.

This is the sole story concerning Lord Peter's secret diplomacy for the War Office, although the canon suggests Wimsey was several times involved in such matters. The title refers to the Comte de Rueil's means of identifying the real Lord Peter.

"The Learned Adventure of the Dragon's Head" (1926)

Lord Peter and his nephew are at an antique bookseller's, and the nephew—Gerald, or Jerry— buys a book. Soon after, a man shows up at Lord Peter's flat, trying to buy that book. Eventually, the story turns into a version of the dying message plot. Like Poe's "The Gold-Bug" (1843) and Ellery Queen's "The Needle's Eye" (1951; collected in *A Calendar of Crime*, 1952), this is a story about pirate treasure. An illustration from the book purchased by Gerald—Munster's *Cosmographia Universalis*—is reproduced in the story.

"The Piscatorial Farce of the Stolen Stomach"

Lord Peter, visiting a friend in Scotland, becomes interested in the friend's inheritance of his uncle's "alimentary organs" in a glass jar. The friend is studying to become a doctor. This is the fourth story in *Lord Peter Views the Body* to involve an inheritance and a will—indeed, in this story Wimsey goes to Somerset House and pays a shilling to read the uncle's will.

"The Unsolved Puzzle of the Man with No Face"

A man in a bathing suit on a rarely visited beach is found strangled with his face disfigured; only his steps in the sand lead to his body. The motif of the body with only its footsteps leading to it is a traditional detective puzzle—as in John Dickson Carr's "Invisible Hands," with his Dr. Gideon Fell as the detective (1957; collected in *The Men Who Explained Miracles*, 1963, and in *Fell and Foulplay*, ed. Douglas G. Greene, 1991). The puzzle is the first part of Sayers's story, solved in a discussion in a train car; then the tale turns to some character sketches and a study of motivations. "Unsolved" in the title has significance.

"The Adventurous Exploit of the Cave of Ali Baba"

The story opens with a newspaper account of Lord Peter Wimsey's death. The tradition of ending books of detective or crime or spy stories with the protagonist's death or apparent death is widespread: e.g., Sir Arthur Conan Doyle's "The Final Problem" (1893; collected in *Memoirs of Sherlock Holmes*, 1894); E. W. Hornung's "The Gift of the Emperor" (collected in *The Amateur Cracksman*, 1899); T. S. Stribling's "A Passage to Benares" (1926; collected in *Clues of the Caribbees*, 1929); and Michael Gilbert's "The Prince of Abyssinia" (collected in *Game without Rules*, 1967). Sayers's story that follows is about a master leader of a criminal gang, who is alluded to near the end of the story as a Moriarty. Lord Peter's conflict with this man is more like Nero Wolfe's conflict with Zeck than Sherlock Holmes with Moriarty. The signifigance of the title is made clear near the end of the story.

"The Image in the Mirror"

Lord Peter Wimsey and Robert Duckworthy, in a lounge in an inn, fall to talking about an H. G. Wells' story, and Duckworthy tells about having been reversed (heart on the wrong side, *etc.*) when he was nearly hit by a bomb in a World War I air-raid. He has had, for a long time, dreams about meeting himself (which Wimsey refers to as meeting a *doppelgänger*) through a mirror. That night the police want to question Duckworthy about the strangulation of a woman.

"The Incredible Elopement of Lord Peter Wimsey"

The story begins in the Basque country of the Pyrenees, where an American doctor and his wife—who suffers, he explains, from premature senility—are living in a small house. About a month and a half later, a magician comes to the area, taking another house. The title is accurate in one sense of *elopement*.

"The Queen's Square"

A costume party at a country estate is the setting, where the costumes are games (e.g., water polo) or game pieces (e.g., cards, chessmen, a billiard table). One of the women is strangled, and the investigation seems to turn on a time-table type of analysis—but not ultimately. The time-table involves an isolated room (not actually locked) at a critical period. An elaborate description of dancing the Sir Roger de Coverley precedes the announcement of the crime. The title refers to a rule about a chess queen; a floor plan of the ballroom area is printed with the story.

"The Necklace of Pearls"

At a Christmas night houseparty in Essex, an expensive pearl necklace is stolen. Lord Peter finds one clue and knows where the pearls are hidden; something said the next morning tells him who the thief is. The story opens with a description of "an old-fashioned Christmas," involving an elaborate dinner followed by Victorian-period games— "Musical Chairs," "Hunt the Slipper," "Dumb Crambo" (involving costumes), and "Animal, Vegetable, and Mineral"—meant to be followed by "Hide and Seek," but the theft intervenes.

*

"In the Teeth of Evidence"

Lord Peter goes to his dentist, Mr. Lamplough, about his "left-hand upper grinder" and then gets concerned with a burnt body, thought to be that of another dentist, which has to be identified by its dental work. The body's teeth are checked against Mr. Lamplough's predecessor's records, and Mr. Lamplough declares they match. The body was found in a car in a garage, and the police next consider the question of whether the death was due to an accident or to suicide.

"Absolutely Elsewhere" (1934)

A middle-aged money-lender is stabbed in the back one evening at his dinner table. Lord Peter has to break an alibi to solve the case. The title comes from Chief-Inspector Parker, of the C.I.D., commenting, "… all the obvious suspects were elsewhere at the time [of the murder]"; Lord Peter replies with a quibble that sets up the first word of the title.

*

"Striding Folly" (1935)

One of the most curious stories in the Wimsey canon, for Mr. Mellilow has a dream that is a symbolic foreshadowing of later events—and Wimsey accepts the precognition with a reference to Lewis Carroll's White Queen. The basic crime story is the murder of a man who is planning to sell a large property to a power company; Mr. Mellilow and the murderee are regular chess opponents, and chess imagery appears in the dream.

"The Haunted Policeman" (1938)

At three o'clock in the morning, after the birth of his first child, Lord Peter meets a policeman who saw (through a mail slot in a front door) a room with a dead body in a No. 13 house on a row of houses; slightly later, both the house number and the room are not to be found. The vanishing locale is a standard motif in mystery puzzles; one example is by John Dickson Carr (under his Carter Dickson pseudonym), "The Crime in Nobody's Room" (1938; collected in *The Department of Queer Complaints*, 1940, and in *Merrivale, March, and Murder*, ed. Douglas G. Greene, 1991), in which a man returns from a party, goes into (he believes) his room in an apartment house, finds some wrong furnishings and a dead body—but when he recovers in the hall from being struck from behind, no apartment on that floor matches the one he saw and none has a dead body.

*

"Talboys"

The only crime solved in this story is the theft of a neighbor's peaches. But much of the story is taken up with theories and practices of childrearing, Lord Peter and Harriet having three sons after seven years of marriage. Their home, Talboys, is the house they came to in *Busman's Honeymoon* (1937) and the subtitle of that novel—*A Love Story with Detective Interruptions*—suggests the tendency here to subordinate the crime element to domestic concerns.

*

"The Young Lord Peter Consults Sherlock Holmes" (broadcast 1954)

Lord Peter, nearly eight years old, visits Holmes about a lost kitten. The story belongs to the "locked room" genre. (The title was given by the publisher; the broadcast speech—part of a celebration of Sherlock Holmes' 100th birthday—had no separate title.)

Montague ("Monty") Egg

The first six stories are from *Hangman's Holiday* (1933) in the order listed; the next five are from *"In the Teeth of Evidence" and Other Stories* (1939) in the order listed.

"The Poisoned Dow '08"

A locked-room puzzle. Lord Borrodale dies in his study from poison after locking himself in. The investigation seems to eliminate all possibilities of introducing the poison into his wine. Mr. Montague ("Monty") Egg, traveling representative for Plummet & Rose, Wines and Spirits, Piccadilly, speaks the first sentence of the story, in this, his first appearance. His first rhymed maxim, from the *Salesman's Handbook*, is "The good will of the maid is nine-tenths of the trade"; his trilby hat is also introduced. Egg had sold the wine to the lord.

"Sleuths on the Scent"

A group of travelers, isolated because of "frost" on the roads, in the bar-parlour of a hotel in a small town near Nottingham, discuss, among other things, a very recent murder, in which an elderly woman had been "bashed" in her home. The radio reports about a man sought for questioning. The titular reference to "scent" refers to a perfume one of the salesmen is selling. Egg observes an inconsistency between an action and a comment by one of the people present.

"Murder in the Morning"

Egg, wishing to sell wine to a wealthy, elderly man, calls at his house in the country, finding him beaten to death by a poker. At an inquest, a witness gives a possible murderer an alibi. Egg observes a coincidence of times (involving a British practice) and thereby explains a mistake in the alibi. (The story mentions that Egg had served two years on the "Western Front"—in other words, on the front lines in World War I.)

"One Too Many"

A vanishing puzzle—in this case, from a train. (The most famous of the fictional vanishings is the untold story of Mr. James Phillimore, who returned to his house for his umbrella and was never seen again. Alluded to in "The Problem of Thor Bridge" [1922; collected in *The Case Book of Sherlock Holmes*, 1927].) A very wealthy businessman disappears from a train between Coventry and London, and his business holdings turn out to have been drained of money before his vanishing. Egg by chance had traveled on that train at the same time, and he is able to explain to a policeman how two may travel on one ticket—something Egg had done to win wagers from friends.

"Murder at Pentecost"

Egg, in Oxford with a letter of introduction to a man at Pentecost College, learns about the recent murder of the Master of that college. His chance encounter with an undergraduate of Pentecost allows him to learn details (another blunt instrument). Egg visits the Bodleian Library during his investigation. Partly a time-schedule mystery; partly a variant on the Least Suspect Person. (Pentecost is not the name of an actual college at Oxford.)

"Maher-Shalal-Hashbaz"

Egg meets a young woman "of sixteen or so" who is going to sell her pet ginger cat because her family needs the money. The reason why a man—"John Doe"—is buying a cat for ten shillings is slowly revealed, but the story is more one of suspense than Sayers's usual intellectually-solved puzzle. "Mahler-Shalal-Hasbaz" is the name of the cat because he "makes haste to the spoil." (The Hebrew name "Maher-Salal-Has-Baz"—given by Isaiah to one of his sons for symbolic purposes— means "The spoil speeds; the prey hastes"; see Isaiah 8.1-4.)

*

"A Shot at Goal"

In his office one evening, a mill owner has his head bashed in with a heavy ashtray. Several people are unhappy with him, and Egg points to the killer by correctly interpreting a fragment of a letter found in the murderee's hand. This is a Dying Message plot of a sort, but the mill owner had not intended the message.

"Dirt Cheap" (1936)

An interesting allusion appears to "Murder in the Morning": Inspector Monk in this story knows

Inspector Ramage in that, and so has heard of Egg. Egg refers to the earlier event as "a little problem about a garage clock"—and this story is going to turn on the sound of a clock striking that Egg hears in his hotel room. Again, it is a question of an alibi being overturned. (In this story Egg's body is described as "plump"; he is "suitably shocked" at a pornographic photo—he seems to have retained a moral sensibility despite war experience and life as a traveling salesman.)

"Bitter Almonds" (1939)

An elderly man is found dead from a prussic acid poisoning; the obvious suspect is his son, who is planning to marry an actress—for which his father had threatened to disinherit him. A nephew is also involved, and the inquest is reported in some detail. Egg, who attended the inquest about his client's death, goes to the coroner after doing some checking and explains what really happened. The solution is based on esoteric knowledge—although appropriate for Egg to have.

"False Weight"

A salesman is killed—head battered in—in the bar-parlour of a hotel; another salesman was quarreling with him the previous evening. The interpretation of events turns on the time of death; an eight-day grandfather clock is partly tipped over and stopped at 11:10. The title refers to one of the weights in the clock. (One of the salesman has a couple of wives, at least; Egg says, in answer to a police inspector's assumption that all salesmen are such womanizers,

"No wedding-bells for Monty Egg." In the context, probably a denial of a series of mistresses also.)

"The Professor's Manuscript" (1939)

Egg is reading a newspaper with a variety of sensational stories in it at the first of the tale; then he calls upon a Professor Pindar, recently moved into a large house, looks at his library while waiting, and sells him some ports and burgundies. From what he has heard and seen, Egg later is moved to ask some questions about Professor Pindar's *bona fides*. The three clues to the mystery are openly presented. (Egg is twice referred to as young in the story; he says he occasionally reads "a crook yarn or something of that kind.") In this last of the Montague Egg stories, a reference appears to what would today be called an Opinion Piece in a newspaper titled "Can Commercial Travellers be Christians?" —thus tying together Sayers's interests in Egg and in religion.

Smith and Smith: Removals

Crime stories, not detective stories. An organization called Smith and Smith: Removals kills persons who are obstacles to their clients' lives. The members of Smith and Smith in the second story are Mr. Smith, Mr. Smyth, Mr. Smythe, Dr. Schmidt, and Miss Smith; the latter does not appear in the first story. These are presumably meant to be pseudonyms. Smith and Smith is located at a house with poplar trees in both stories. The first story has never been published; the second appears in *"In the Teeth of Evidence" and Other Stories* (1939).

"The House of the Poplars" (unpublished; written about 1928)

> The obstacle removed in this story is a wife. The extreme stereotyping of some Jewish characters may keep the story from being published—and may have kept it from publication originally. A copy is in the Wade Center, Wheaton College, Wheaton, Illinois.

*

"The Leopard Lady"

> The obstacle in this story is a nephew, whose removal allows the male protagonist to inherit a large estate. Possibly the nephew's comments about meeting the fairy queen with two leopards inspired Anthony Boucher's story "Mr. Lupescu" (1945; collected in *The Compleat Werewolf*, 1969, and in *The Compleat Boucher: The Complete Short Science Fiction and Fantasy of Anthony Boucher*, ed. James A Mann, 1998). In both stories a child seems to have a fantasy friend (named in the title of each story) and a murder takes place—but a final twist removes Boucher's story from Sayers's approach. Other well-known genre stories about children's fantasy friends, such as John Collier's "Thus I Refute Beelzy" (1940; collected in *Presenting Moonshine*, 1941, *A Touch of Nutmeg*, 1943, and *Fancies and Goodnights*, 1951), do not have the crime-fiction emphasis of Sayers and Boucher.

The Situations of Judkin

Whether a single story, given the author's intention, should be placed with her series or her miscellaneous short stories is moot. Here it may be considered a transitional work. First published in the present book (2005).

"The Travelling Rug"

A fairly-clued mystery of the explained-away supernatural, in which a new maid (the narrator) comes to a house supposedly haunted by a poltergeist. The title page of Sayers's manuscript shows that the story was planned as the first of a series.

Non-Serial Stories

The first two stories appear, in this sequence, in *Hangman's Holiday* (1933); the next ten stories appear, in this sequence, in *"In the Teeth of Evidence" and Other Stories* (1939)—"The Leopard Lady" originally appeared between the final two stories. Most of these non-series stories end with an ironic twist.

"The Man Who Knew How" (1932)

A "Biter Bit" plot with a second reversal. It begins with a train conversation about a poison that is stimulated by a hot bath, and one of the men on the train becomes obsessed with keeping track of bath-tub deaths. A few satiric comments about detective novels appear in the train conversation.

"The Fountain Plays"

A story about blackmail and murder. The opening scene is a gathering of a host, his daughter, and some guests in a private garden with a fountain; the fountain's recycling of water becomes, at the end of the story, a symbol of the plot.

*

"The Milk-Bottles" (1932)

The first part of the story is told, in the third person, largely from the point of view of a *Morning Star* reporter; this first part follows a sequence of events, beginning with milk bottles not being taken in and ending with the suspicion that a wife has been murderer by her husband. The second part reveals the truth.

"Dilemma" (broadcast 1934)

A discussion of ethical dilemmas in a hotel near a fishing area: which of two actions would one choose to do, given the need to act immediately. Four examples are given, each involving a human life *versus* something valuable in another way. The first two examples are theoretical.

"An Arrow o'er the House" (1934)

The story of an unsuccessful writer of thrillers-cum-detective novels, his secretary, and a campaign to soften up a publisher for the author's current typescript. The campaign goes awry. (The title of the story—the proposed title of the unsuccessful author's next book—is from *Hamlet*.)

"Scrawns"

A maid, having taken a position without an interview, arrives at Scrawns (the name of the house) in the late afternoon. The details are in the Gothic tradition: a huge and ugly cook, her husband with part of his face gone, a man lying very still in an upstairs bed, and (less Gothic) a loud and vulgar owner of the house and his faint and tremulous wife. The maid flees before the night is over.

"Nebuchadnezzar"

The title of the story refers to a pantomime game, rather like a very elaborate charades done in scenes, which in the story is being played by a group of people in a London flat. Much of the story is told in the consciousness of one of those in the audience.

"The Inspiration of Mr. Budd" (1926)

A hair-dresser has a man whom he believes to be a wanted criminal come into his shop to get his hair and moustache dyed, saying his girlfriend does not like his red hair. The hair-dresser is the one who has the titular inspiration.

"Blood Sacrifice" (1936)

A young, serious playwright had his script taken by an older actor-manager who has turned it into an emotional crowd-pleaser. The playwright is making money but feels he has lost his reputation. Much of the story follows his thoughts, and the story is more of a psychological study than most of

Sayers's tales.   The title refers to a blood transfusion near the end of the story after a car accident.   (Although this story first appeared in a magazine, it was written for an anthology titled *Six against the Yard* [1936], which contains a collection of stories of "perfect crimes," each followed by an afterword by Ex-Superintendent Cornish of the C.I.D., explaining how the police could have, possibly or probably, solved the crime.)

"Suspicion" (1933)

Mr. Mummery has stomach upsets, has a new cook at his home, and reads news stories about a woman escaping capture who poisoned her employers.

"The Cyprian Cat"

A man (in jail, it is implied) tells his lawyer the story of his visit to a friend and the friend's wife, and of his being bothered most nights by a large Cyprian cat outside the hotel—he has always hated cats. He buys a small gun at a nearby town. If one remembers Sayers's comment in the "Mystery and Horror" area of her introduction to *The Second Omnibus of Crime* (1932; published in Britain the previous year as *Great Short Stories of Detection, Mystery and Horror—Second Series*) that the old-fashioned ghost-story "makes no use of the disagreeable hint; it leaves too little to the imagination," one may regard with respect Sayers's indirection here.

Facsimile of Dorothy L. Sayers's
manuscript of
The Travelling Rug

The Situations of Judkin

1.
THE
TRAVELLING RUG

by
Dorothy L. Sayers

Yes, madam, it's quite true I've been had in great many situations in a short time, but then you see, madam, I'm what you might call a specialist. I was just reading in the paper the other day that this was an age of specialisation, so I'm only ~~being going~~ moving with the times, as the saying goes.

I was all of ten years in my first place. That was with old Miss Marrable of Blathwick ~~Hall~~ indoor. There was six servants kept in those days, & I started as kitchen-maid when I was only fifteen. I was second house-maid when the War started, & then first house-maid, & then the mistress had to reduce the staff, owing to so much of her money being in foreign investments. Mr Cliddings, the butler, was called up, too; so part of the house was closed & I stayed on as house-parlourmaid, with a girl under me. Mr Cliddings taught me the silver & table work, & of course I'd picked up a good bit about cooking when I was working in the kitchen; so when the crash came & Miss Marrable had to sell ~~everything~~ the place & take a little house in Rutherstane, I was able to stay on with her as cook-general. She was a proper lady, was Miss Marrable, one of the real old-fashioned sort — you don't find many of them nowadays. A better mistress you couldn't wish for & I wouldn't have left her, not for any money. But she

began to break up fast, poor dear, after we left Blathwick
+ she died in 1922. That's her silver tea-service she
left me; I'm very proud of that. Real Queen Anne, +
valuable, so they tell me — but of course I wouldn't part
with it, not if it was ever so.

Well, I was twenty-five when Miss Marsable passed
away, though I was very fond of her, of course it was
a very quiet situation towards the end. So I told Miss
Carrick up at the Registry that I'd like something with a
little more life about it. I had plenty to pick + choose from,
people couldn't get maids then for love or money, but you
see, I'd been trained to good service, + I didn't want to
go to any of these new-rich as they call them, + the real
gentle people couldn't afford much in the way of wages.

Well, Miss Carrick had given me a list as long as
your arm + was shutting up the book, when she began to
laugh + said, casual-like: "If you want something lively,
Jane, you might like to try Mrs Festone's. She's a real
lady + she doesn't mind what she pays. She wants anything anybody
she can get — cook, house-parlour-maid, cook-general —
whatever you like to call yourself. It's a pretty place,
Manneling House in Norfolk, two miles from the town, but
a car kept + good tea service. And the chauffeur's
still there — at present."

"Oh!" I said. "And the rest of them left at short notice, is that it? What's the catch, Miss Carrick?"

"There've got a poltergeist," said Miss Carrick, & laughed again. Miss Carrick is very straight with her girls & always tells you if there's anything funny about a place.

Well, I did not know then what a poltergeist was, but Miss Carrick explained that it was a kind of a ghost-affair that threw crockery & furniture about. "It's probably some silly person playing tricks," she said, "but the staff have got frightened, & run away. Miss Fastowe wants a good, sensible girl with a head on her shoulders. Do you fancy tackling the poltergeist? There's only two in the family — H^rs Fastowe & her invalid niece. She tells us she does any nursing that's needed herself, so you won't have to undertake that."

Well, I thought it over. By what Miss Carrick told me, the poltergeist did no harm to human beings, & though the household didn't sound exactly gay, it didn't sound dull, either. Besides, the money was good — & then, of course, there was the chauffeur. I mean, when you get to twenty-five, you don't want to miss anything.

Well, I got to the station all right, & there was the chauffeur to meet me, & believe me, madam, he was as per advertisement. I mean to say, if he had me on the films he could have done the long, long kiss in the moonlit garden + given Clark Gable + Ramon Novarro a start + a beating. Features like a greek god, as they say in the stories + moving with the feline grace of a panther, only I never could abide them animals.

"You the young lady for Monseoring Horne?" he says. And I said, "I'm the new housemaid". Mrs Chiddings always taught us to be particular how we answered, ever since a temporary parlour-maid was shown into the drawing-room by mistake. "My name's Judkin," I went on, to make myself quite clear.

"I don't like the name," says he, ~~kind~~ sparkling at me ~~sort of stooping down to~~ ~~look under my hat~~ Haven't you got a prettier one? ~~What comes~~ ~~else before the Judkin?~~

"Miss Judkin to you," says I, because panther or no panther, I thought he was ~~taking things a little too much~~ taking things a bit for granted. Besides, at the ~~Hall~~ the chauffeur was always expected to keep his proper distance.

"All right, Miss Judkin," says he, smiling away like a tooth-paste advertisement — lovely white teeth he had, too. "You're a young lady of spirit, aren't you? I like 'em spirited." And you'll need to be, too, at our place.

And off he went to get my trunk.

On the way to the house I asked him about the poltergeist.

"Oh, you've heard about that, have you?" says he. "And
you're not afraid? There's lots of them would be. But I could see
at once, you're not that sort."

"What's there to be afraid of?" said I. "It doesn't hurt
anybody, does it?"

"Not so far," he said. "Not hurt anybody. No. It
might play a few pranks in your bedroom, like pulling the
clothes off the bed, but you wouldn't mind that, would you?"

"Seeing it's November," said I, "I should mind quite a bit."

"Perhaps it'll resist the temptation," says he, "though
I don't know that I would, in its place."

He looked round in a way I didn't like. He had
beautiful curly eye-lashes.

"You keep your eye on the road," I said, a bit
sharp, like. "I'm much more afraid of a motor-smash than
I am of poltergeists."

After that he told us a bit more. It seems the house
has a reputation for being haunted before Mrs Fastwe
came to live there. That was six months before, & the trouble
had started almost at once, in a small way. Just little
things at first, like doors opening unexpectedly, the
pots & pans being all put higgledy-piggledy in the night.

After a time, the ghost seemed to get more confidence, & started to throw things about in broad daylight — quite peevy things. The servants didn't like it, & were always leaving, on some excuse or other. The final upset had happened about a week before when a silver dish-cover had come walking at of the pantry to meet the parlour-maid. She ran away, yelling, of course, fit to raise the roof, & just as she got into the kitchen, she met the cook was just coming out to see what all the surprise was about. They were standing together in the doorway when a big copper fish-kettle came hopping off the high mantel-piece, right down where cook had just been standing. That finished the two women. They went out by hysterics, & my friend the chauffeur ran in from the garage, thinking the place was a-fire. By the time he'd set them down & thrown water over them & been up to reassure Mrs Fairlove, who was sitting with her niece, the dish-cover had hung itself up on the hat-stand. The cook & the maid couldn't stand that, so they took themselves off next day without notice or wages, + my friend the chauffeur (his name, or so he told me, was Ludovic Maltravers, a thing I don't believe & my late mistress never would have permitted), he had to do all the work of the house for the rest six days, with only a woman from the village coming in & leaving before it got dark.

"You've been here all the time, then," I said. "You must be terribly brave."

He liked that, of course. But he admitted he hadn't been there all the time, only the last four months. The man before him had left after words with Mrs Faxtone on account of water having been poured into his petrol tank. They didn't realise about the poltergeist then, & he thought somebody had been playing a trick on him, while Mrs Faxtone thought he'd done it himself to get out of taking the car out in the rain & having it to clean afterwards.

I hadn't been interviewed by Mrs Faxtone. She couldn't leave her niece — the girl having something wrong with her spine & not being able to get out of bed — & she was too trustful to get any maid to bother very much what I was like, so she took me on my good reference. The first minute I saw her, I recognised that she was a lady, all right, but of the helpless sort. I don't mean she couldn't see to things in the house & nurse her niece & so on; but she was a lady with no self-confidence. Been used to having everything made up for her, I reckon, by Mr Faxtone, whoever he was when he was alive. She was fair & small & must have been pretty once in a fluffy kind of way, & I could see she was dead frightened of the poltergeist & still more frightened that I should be frightened & leave.

She said she hoped I should be comfortable & work well & I said I would try to give satisfaction. And she asked what my name was. So I said, "My late mistress called me Juskin, madam." So she asked, what was my Christian name, & I said, "Eurydice, madam" — which was true, my Dad having read that name in a book just before I was christened & taken a fancy to it, but my mother had different ideas, so they made it Jane Eurydice. That rather took Mrs Fastone aback, as you might say, because nobody could have a servant called Eurydice, & neither Urry nor Dicey sounds very well as a cut-short. So she said, "Oh, very well, Juskin." That showed me where I was with her (Miss Marluble would have said: "That won't do; you had better answer to Susan"), & it was one in the eye for Mr Ludovic Maltravers, since he couldn't get hold of my name through hearing me called by it.

Mrs Fastone showed me the house, which was ᵃˡᵉ very nice, in an old-fashioned style, & told me what my work would be. The daily woman was to come in to cook till Mrs Fastone was suited, & I was to do all the house & parlour work, except the brass, which was Maltravers's job. I thought Mrs Fastone looked a bit very as every time we passed anything like a big vase, & once when a door slammed she jumped right into the air; but the furniture didn't do anything out of the way, + finally I was taken up to see the sick niece, Miss Blazey. She was on a kind of couch in a big, bright bedroom + looked thin + peaky + a bit peevish, to my thinking. She had sandy hair + very big, grey eyes, with a bright, intense look in them. She spoke nicely to me, + said she ~~hoped~~ I should be happy ~~+ do~~ + settle down with them. And when I said, "Yes, miss; I'm sure I'll do my best," she looked very hard at me, as if she had her doubts. Mrs Fastnor didn't say anything to me about the poltergeist, ~~but~~ + of course it wasn't my ~~Maltravers told~~ place to mention it; but Maltravers told me Miss Blazey knew nothing about it. So far, nothing had happened in her room, except a funny sort of perfume, now + again, + they kept it from her, for fear of upsetting her. But I wasn't so sure that she didn't know anything. I know fright when I see it, + that girl was frightened, believe me. So then I went upstairs to change my dress + start on my work.

We got along pretty well that night. I suppose the poltergeist was kind of sizing me up + considering what he had best do with me, because, bar half a dozen tumblers suddenly falling off the dresser without a hand touching them, + the gong in the hall ringing very loud when Mrs Fastnor was at dinner + Ludovic helping me serve, nothing out of the way happened when the gong rang, I ran at quick, with a vegetable dish in my hand, but there wasn't anybody in the hall, & the gong-stick was hanging up quite quiet in its place. Thank goodness the ghost left the dinner alone. the daily woman had got a casserole ready, & I did some potatoes to go with it & there was jam tarts to follow, which (though I cald have made lighter myself, if it had been left to me.

I locked my bedroom door that night — not so much on account of the ghost so much as of Ludovic, who slept in the house to protect us from whatever it was. I was tired with my journey & slept sound; though I had an idea there were noises going on somewhere in the house. As well there might have been, because next morning we found all the kitchen pots & pans stacked up on the table in a kind of Tower. The ghost must have put in a good hard bit of work: it took me over half an hour to get the mess straightened out & find the pan for the bacon & eggs.

I'd done all the breakfasts & taken them up by the time Mrs Poot arrived. She was a thin, bony sort of woman, with her hair all wisps & the most graveyard way of talking you ever heard. She came in on me when I was in the drawing-room, arranging a rug to cover over a big brown stain on the carpet near the fireplace.

"Morning," she said. "You the new girl? Well, I only 'opes as you'll find the place agreeable."

"And why not?" says I. "The mistress seems a very nice lady."

"Ah," said Mrs. Poot. "She's all right. It's this 'ouse. But there! You'll find it soon enough. It's a 'ouse with a long memory. It ain't no use you trying to river up that there stain. It don't stay rivered."

"What do you mean?" says I.

"You can river up that there stain with that there sug," said Mrs. Poot, "as many time as you like. But sooner or later it'll creep away off of it. There's things as can't be 'id."

"It's a nasty stain," says I, a bit short, like "why can't they send the carpet to the cleaners?"

"So they 'ave, dearie, so they 'ase. But the stain comes back. It come back in the old lady's time. It's a nasty stain, you're right there. Blood!" said Mrs. Poot, leaning on her broom-handle & relishing the word as you wiges say. "Blood, dearie. You can't clean it at & you can't river it up. The poor senseless sug 'ull creep away off of it. You'll see if it don't."

"Whose blood?" says I. Because I've known plenty of stains come back after they been dry-cleaned, but they weren't blood.

"There was a man killed here once, dear," said Mrs Poot. "Murder, it was. Years ago. If ya lift up the carpet, ya'll find 'is life-blood in the boards. It soaks up through the carpet. If ya was to put a new carpet down, however the stain 'ud come a-creeping up again afore ya was many months older."

"Have they tried a new carpet?" I asked.

"No," said Mrs Poot, a bit grudgingly. "They ain't. Uo the old carpet. But a new ne would be just the same. Stains of murder won't never come out — everybody knows that."

"I don't believe a word of it," said I, patting the rug back into its place.

"Ah!" said Mrs Poot. "Yo're young. Ya've a lot to learn yet. Well, I must be takin' me life in me 'and & gettin' on with me work. I don't so much mind the kittles a-flyin' about — you can dodge kittles; but when it come to heavy wardrobes a-tryin' to squedge ya up ag'in the wall, forty shillin's a week don't 'ardly seem worth the risk."

Shilings a week! Did ya ever hear the like, madam, for a country charwoman? Eight hours a day, with three meals given! I made up my mind then & there

I could do the work myself, with Ludovic & save the expense of Mrs Poot. I'd have given that myself, if I had it, to keep her ugly face out of my kitchen the weal of, shaking her head, to get herself her breakfast (& to surprising what she could put away & stay so thin), & I went on with my dusting.

The drawing-room was re of the old-fashioned sort, with a lot of china about it, especially on the mantelpiece which had one of them looking-glasses over it, all shelves; & there was a sight of vases & little figures on whal-nots & chiffoniers all round the room. I made a good job of it though, getting up on a chair to do the chimney ornaments, which looked as if they hadn't been touched for months. The fire wasn't burning very well — the coal-merchant must have thought Mrs Forlove a soft proposition — but I knelt down & had a good go at it with the bellows. After that, I had to go over some of the mantel piece again, but in the end I got it to go nice & cheerful. I turned back at the door before I left it to have a look at it & was thinking how pretty & bright it looked, when I saw something that give me quite a turn.

There was that queer stain showing again under the end of the hearth-rug!

Of corse, it didn't take me a moment to tell myself that I must somehow have kicked the rug up while I was blowing the fire, & I soon had it straight. But I felt a bit of a fool, & I didn't say anything about it to Mrs Poot. But over here our elevenses, which she ate hearty of, I did get something out of her about the house & family. It seems the old lady that used to live there was Mrs Fastove's great-aunt & she died & left her the house & an income to keep it up; but by the way the will was worded, if Mrs Fastove left the house, the money would pass away from her to Miss Blazey. Mr Fastove had been a clerical gentleman, & left his widow very poor when he died; so she had to carry out the terms of the will, preferring the poltergeist, I suppose, to living dependent on her niece. Neither Mrs Poot nor Ludovic had a good word to say for Miss Blazey, & I made out she was one of those exacting invalids that nothing ever pleases. Not but what you couldn't help feeling sorry for her, lying there helpless, & having to be lifted from her bed to the sofa. They didn't rightly know what had caused the injury to her spine, only that she'd had a fall when she was at school; but the doctors said the trouble was due to the shock more than to the fall.

Mrs Fastove had company that afternoon: the vicar & his lady come to call. I took the tea up to the drawing-room, & I couldn't hardly believe my eyes when I seen that ugly old stain had come peeping out from under the rug again. I was so incensed with the stupid thing, I nearly made an excuse & set it to right then & there; only I could see Mrs. Fastone looking at it in a nervous sort of way out of the corner of her eyes, as if she hoped it wouldn't be noticed so I didn't draw attention to it. But I promised myself I'd take a hammer & tacks to it that night & see if the poltergeist could get over that.

My next job was to take up Miss Blazey's tray to her. She wasn't so well that day & was keeping in bed. The minute I got in, "Do you smell anything, Judkin?" she says to me. "Nothing, miss," I says, "only that joss-stick you've been burning or whatever it is." "It's not a joss-stick," she says, "it's the perfume of the dead. It wasn't here an hour ago, but it comes every day. Aunt Angela pretends it comes in from the landing, but I know they mean it for me. Is there anything burning outside, Judkin? Tell me the truth, because Aunt Angela won't."

Well, I thought I'd better mind my step, so I says: "I really couldn't say, miss; I'll go & see." But though you could smell it outside, it wasn't half so strong as it was in the room. So I searched every corner of the place, peeping into all the vases & looking in the fireplace & under the bed, & even, at the young lady's request, in the bed — for the scent seemed to hang all about her — that, naturally, you couldn't very well burn a thing like that under the bedclothes. "Don't you fret, miss," I said, "I'll find the thing, never fear, some day when you're up. It smells just like one of them little incense-cones you buy at the chemist's."

"You'll never find it," she says, "it comes from the other side of the veil. How do you like this house, Jaskin? It has a life of its own, & I'm afraid of it. Why doesn't Aunt Angela tell the truth? I can hear it muttering & walking in the night. I tell you, it's the house of the dead, & the dead are not happy. They can't rest. If the dead could rest, I should be at rest one day."

She had an awful queer look in her eyes, like as if she was scared out of her wits — & just as I was going to say something, there comes a most awful banging & clattering, like fifty thousand million tin trays falling through a greenhouse. "Oh, my god!" calls out Miss Brazey, "what's that?". "Sounds like something falling down, miss," says I, tries taking it calm, like, though I could hear somebody screaming like anything down below." "Go & pick it up," I says, & I forwards out & looks over the banisters. Which I see made no sense down stairs in a hurry. There was Mr Vicar standing in the hall, shrieking his head

off & the kitchen gentleman holding her up, & Mrs
Fastose wringing her hands ~~no while you~~ about &
Ludovic running in with his face like a sheet & Ludovic running in from the garden with the ~~rope~~ string
he'd been making out a new bow with trailing behind
him & Mr Poot after him — her having run out the
back way yelling ~~"fire &~~ & blue murder — & there
was a huge great brass pot of that Indian sort,
(Benares work they call it, don't they?) that stood on
the top landing, with an aspidistra in it, staying in to hall & the great
mirror opposite the front door all smashed into stars
& stripes where the ~~Benares~~ ~~brass~~ pot had hit it.

"Oh, dear me," ~~madam~~ & myself, says I, "somebody's going
to have bad luck, & I hope it's the poltergeist."

So Mrs Vicar points her finger at me, all shaking,
& screechs out: "Did you do that?"

"Well, I thought as maybe it wouldn't make matters,
~~pleasanter if I took the blame~~ ~~to make matters pleasanter~~, So I says: "Yes, madam, & I'm
sure I'm very sorry. How it came to slip out of my hand
I can't think & I'm sure it's a mercy there was nobody
hurt." And I picks up the pot, as was all dinted in, &
I says to Mrs Fastose, "Mind the broken glass, madam," I
says. "I'll just fetch my dust-pan & brush & have
it all swept up in a minute." The mistress looked very
hard and queer at me, but she plucked her courage up

(& that showed she was a real lady after all) & she says: "It was most careless of you, Jenkin. You might easily have killed somebody." And as I went off for the dustpan, I heard her apologising to the lady & gentleman.

So I swept up the bits & then nipped upstairs to tell Miss Bleezey it was only Mrs Pook had an accident with the banana pot (thinking Mrs P might take her share of the trouble, & not mentioning the mirror), & when I came down again, the guests were just leaving & I showed them out. So Mrs Footsole says to me: "Did you really do that, Jenkin?" And I said, "No, madam, but I thought it best to say I did." And she said, "Quite right, Jenkin, that was sensible of you." And she never said another word, but went straight up to Miss Bleezey, & I went into the drawing-room & stared at that stupid rug & the stain on the carpet.

It wasn't what I should have called a suitable rug for the room. It was a lot newer than the carpet & had one of those kind of up-to-date patterns all in straight lines, while the carpet was all cabbage-roses. I guessed it had been got to cover up the stain in place of a ~~narrower~~ shorter one. I had a good look at that rug, front & back, & then I decided I wouldn't tack it down, but give it one more chance to behave itself. Only this time I turned it round with its front edge against the fender. It looked a bit funny that way, because the pattern was a kind of sunrise affair, with rays shooting out from a round thing at one side, & of course I could see it was meant to look as if the rays were coming out from the fireplace, like. All the same, I turned it round. I knew, if they noticed anything, they'd just think the new maid was being stupid. After that, I went up to the top landing & looked at the place the Benares pot had fallen from. It had used to stand on one of three mahogany pedestals, close to the banisters, & the top of the pedestal came just above the banister-rail. A silly place, I thought, to stand a thing like that. Anyone knocking against it might have tipped it over — only, of course, there hadn't been anybody there. I leant over & looked down into the hall to see where the thing had gone over — & then I jumped right up in the air. Something touched me on the back of the neck — just like a cold, icy finger it was. I just stopped myself letting out a yell. I was glad, next minute, I hadn't been such a fool. It was only the landing window open & a gust of rain blowing in; but it just showed me I was getting jumpy.

"Now then, Jane Turpdice," I said to myself, "pull yourself together, my girl." And I shut the window & went down to the kitchen.

Well, it seems as if the ghost had made up its mind that evening I was the kind of person that needed strong measures. If I was to tell you the way that have behaved I should never have done. First it was the gong ringing, on & off, on & off, & then it was doors banging & things tumbling down & once something went off with a great bang in the garden. The poor mistress gave up all pretence that things were as they should be. She & I & Ludovic kept running round the place with the pokers, & every time, when we got to where the noise had come from, something would start off in a different part of the house. Chronic it was that with the noises & the running about, Miss Bracey started to sing out before like mad & said she was too frightened to be left alone. So then Mrs Fastive went to sit with her, & Ludovic & I went round the place by ourselves; which I didn't like, because it bad enough to be hunting for ghosts in the middle of the night without anybody trying to kiss you every time he got you into a dark corner. And then, just as the clock struck midnight, every light in the house went out, & I had to go down with Ludovic & hold the torch while he replaced the main fuse. I scratched his face, though, & he wasn't too pleased about it. That was the last of the disturbances, & we all went to bed.

I did a good bit of thinking that night. I don't know why it was, but I couldn't believe in a ghost that would take out the main fuse out of its box & put in a bit of fuse wire in its place. It seemed to me, a real ghost ought to be able to work a blow-out without making use of a screw-driver. Ludovic hadn't drawn attention to the fuse-wire. I suppose he thought, being a woman, I should be too stupid to understand; but when Miss Hurlstone had her little house I'd learnt all about fuses. I could even connect up a new lamp or mend the switch if I was put to it. I'm neat with my hands, Dad having been a joiner & cabinet-maker. In fact, I'd have had my suspicions of Ludovic, only I couldn't see why he should want to play at ghosts. And besides, he couldn't have rung the gong in the hall while he was helping me in the dining-room.

But next day I came down with my mind made up to do a bit of house-cleaning. I'm sure the place needed it. I was up at five & starting to work in the kitchen, & the dust on the top of the dresser was a thing you wouldn't hardly believe. There were one or two holes in the walls, too, but I got a bit of putty from Ludovic's tool-shed & stopped them up; & while I was hunting about there I found a box full of that very fine catgut that Miss Marrable's great-nephew, Mr John, used to use for making his trout-casts. I cut off a good long piece of that + put it in my pocket, thinking it might come in handy for an idea I had in my mind. I'd done all the kitchen + scullery ~~thing~~ thoroughly by breakfast time, with the help of Serafina the black cat. An intelligent, sensible creature she was, + must have seen a lot, going about at night the way she did. She + me was great friends. I had her in with me while I scrubbed out the outside larder, + she was as good as gold, sitting up on the shelf like a little image + never offering to touch the milk nor nothing. I was singing away at my work, when I heard Mrs Poot come ~~along the passage~~ + go into the larder, leaving the scullery door open behind her. She hadn't been there five minutes when she let out a big scream, + when I came in to see what was up, there was the big meat-safe skating round the kitchen floor. Funny it did look, I must say, I couldn't hardly help laughing, but I picked up the safe + shows her Serafina sitting inside.

"Thought it was the ghost, did you, Mrs Poot?" says I. "Well, I put one over on you there." And I took the meat-safe back to the larder, leaving her exclaiming + holding her hand to her heart. Serafina came in then + I heard her telling him all about it. He wasn't best pleased, Ludovic wasn't, + came out + told me I didn't ought to play them tricks; I might have been the death of the poor woman. "All right, all right," I says, "Rudolph Valentino, keep your hair on. Mrs Poots seen worse than a poor cat in a meat-safe." And I sloshed a pail of water over the floor, so he had to skip it of the way quick to save those nasty yellow boots of his, too. If Miss Marsuble had seen her chauffeur in them boots like that, she'd have had him on the mat good + proper.

Well, I'd got an appetite for breakfast by that time + it didn't worry me that I didn't seem to be what you might call popular in the kitchen. So after I'd done myself proud on the eggs + bacon + taken up the trays, I set Mrs Poot to turn out the hall + landing + went to dust the drawing-room. And there wasn't no stain showing on the carpet this time, neither. Not but what the heavy thing had been walking all right; only this time it had walked in the other direction, so to speak, + was making for the chiffonier, so that the stain come right under the middle of it instead of at one end. Well, that was all right, so far.

~~Well, that afternoon was very afternoon off, so I asked Mr Forbes could Ludovic drive me into the town to buy some more apples. He said, Yes, certainly, + we had quite a nice~~

& the next thing I wanted to do was to look into that funny smell in Miss Blasey's room. Only it was difficult to have a thorough turn-out there, owing to her being always in her room & not to be disturbed.

I must say, if any girl wants to do pretty much as she likes & no questions asked, she can't do much better than take a situation with a poltergeist. Anything at all that went wrong at Mannering House was put down to the spook. When half a jug of water disappeared from the larder, that was the spook — though I happened to call in on Mrs. Poot that same evening to ask about a bit of laundry wanted doing, & they was having cold mutton for supper. And when the soup was burnt, that was the spook too. And so, when one evening there was a big can of water spilt found in Miss Blasey's bed with the cap half-unscrewed & all the oil leaking into the mattress, that was put down to the spook without any hesitation. I told Mrs. Fastaive there was no can there when I went to make the bed in the morning, & no more there was, for I didn't put it in till I flampht up the hot-water bottles at dinner-time. I found the can there when I went up to turn down the bed & if you'll believe me, I was so misfortunate, pulling the clothes down to see what the trouble was, that I pulled the bottle out & the oil went all over the floor & pretty well ruined a pretty rug that lay by the bed. Of course, Miss Brazey couldn't sleep there with the floor all oily, so we had to get Ludovic Halloway to help carry her in. Such a to-do there was, Miss Brazey had hysterics, screaming out that she knew the house was haunted & poor Mrs Firestone had to tell her the whole story. I was really sorry to have made such a lot of trouble, but I wanted to get that bedroom clear. Ludovic came along when I was stripping the mattress off & wanted to help, but I said I could manage by my self, thank him kindly; & I turned him out & came out my self & locked the door & put the key in my pocket.

The can of oil had passed off so nicely, being all put down to the poltergeist, I thought I'd have another try at producing what the spirit-rapping gentry call a phenomena or two. So when I was doing my kitchen smalls in the garage I'd picked out a big old copper preserving-pan that stood on a high shelf near the kitchen window, & rolled it close to the edge, where a touch would send it over, & I got Ludovic's bit of fishing-tackle & slipped it through an handle & ran both ends out through a chink at the top of the window & let them hang down by the wall near the rain-water butt. You couldn't notice anything either inside or outside, the gut being so fine, & now I thought would be a good time to try it. So I waited till Ludovic had settled himself down in his chair by the fire & put in one of his everlasting cigarettes, & said something about getting a jug of rain water to wash my hair with. He didn't pay much attention, so I went out & found the two ends of the gut & pulled hard. My aunt! You never heard such a row! The pan came down beautiful & bounced off the edge of the flour-bin & Ludovic jumped up as if he'd a-been shot. I was that excited, I almost forgot to let go one end of the gut & haul it out, & if he'd been quick he'd have seen it go; but he stood there like a stuck pig, & the line come away beautiful & I bundled it up & pushed the lot into the water-butt before I came running in to ask what the noise was. "My God!" says he, "did you hear that?" "Of course I heard it," says I, "not being deaf. What's the matter with you? It's only the poltergeist — you ought to be used to that by this time." Well, just then the drawing-room bell rang & I went along to see what the mistress wanted. It seemed Miss Beazey had asked her aunt to

make her a brandy-flip & Mrs Fastвсе was coming out
to the kitchen with the decanter when she suddenly came
over faint, hearing the clatter, & had to go back &
set down. "You do look white, madam," I said,
"& so she did, poor soul. "Take a little glass yourself,
madam," I said, "+ I'll make the flip in a minute
& run up with it. I used to make brandy flip for my
late mistress," I said, "+ you can trust me, madam."
So back I went to the kitchen & whisked up the egg &
put the sugar & brandy to it & started upstairs.
And just as I got to the turn o' the landing, who
should I see but my lord the Ludovic, coming out
of the spare room where Miss Blazey. "Well," I
says to myself, "if that don't beat the band! And
what are you doing up here?" I says to him. "Oh,"
he says, "I just went up to tell the young lady not
to be frightened, it was only a saucepan fallen
down in the scullery." "Saucepan to you," I says.
"Miss Blazey couldn't hear nothing this side of
the house. You keep your saucepans till they're
wanted, + your sauce too," I says And I took
the flip in, & Miss Blazey said nothing to me nor
me to her, not being my place, but like the monkey
I thought all the more. Especially when, coming out again

with the tray, there's his nibs trying the door of Miss Brazey's own bedroom. "Well & what next?" I said to him. "Oh," says he, "I thought I might have dropped my cigarette lighter out of my pocket when I went in to help with Miss Brazey." "Oh, indeed?" says I; "well, I'll have a hunt for it when I turns the room out to-morrow." "Be a sport, Judy," he says (that being the name he'd made up for me out of Tuckim, "let's go in & have a look now." "What's the hurry?" says I. "Won't a box of matches do for you for to-night? Anybody'd think you'd done a murder in there & left your finger-prints about." That shut him up all right. "Well," I thinks to myself, "he's left something there he don't want us to find, & he went in to ask Miss Brazey if she had another key." And then it came over me, there might be another boy in the house to fit that fork after all, & I'd better have a look round before anybody else got in. So when Ludovic had gone off downstairs, I got a torch & went into the room to see what I could find. And it didn't take me so long, neither; because, when I'd got the soiled mattress, the underlay, stripped off the bed, there, if you'll believe me, was a little china ash-tray perched in one of the angle-irons underneath the spring, & a little grey grains of ash in it, like the burnt-out ghost of one of those incense cones. You couldn't possibly see it when the bed was made up, not even if you crawled underneath; & I knew otherwise been they when I made the bed in the morning. It seemed funny to me how anybody could have put it there without Miss Brazey noticing. I didn't touch it; only when I went

Anyhow I left the bedroom key, careless-like, in the drawer. The ghost was pretty active about the house that night — spiteful he was, too, filling the saucepans with soot + putting the salt in the castor-sugar — + when I started in to do the bedroom in the morning, the key was where I'd left it, but the little cone of ash + the ~~No-No~~ they were napoo, as they used to say in the war.

Of course, Miss Brazey wanted to get back into her own room; so I put on a mattress out of one of the other rooms, + sent the soiled one to the cleaners' with the bedside rug, but I brought up the drawing-room rug + put it by the bed. I don't know what Mrs Faotone thought about that. She didn't make any remark, + after all, the drawing-room could do quite well without a hearthrug for a few days. The only thing I was afraid of was that the proper rug might come back before the ghost did the gong trick again; but I was lucky. It wasn't ~~too~~ more than two days later, when I was waiting at dinner, when the gong went off, "Boom!" ~~I was carrying the joint in at the moment,~~ ~~I got the joint in my hands, the moment,~~ + I just chose to rush into Ludovic's hands + said, "Hold that!" + I ran upstairs like a lamplighter as they say, though I never see one of them do such a thing. I burst into Miss Brazey's room without knocking. She was lying in her bed reading a book, + she looked rather scared to see me come

rushing in that way. "What's the matter, Jukin?" she says.
And I took a look at the rug by the bedside & I says, "I
see you've been out of bed, miss. I'm sure I'm very happy
to congratulate you on your recovery. the mistress will be
pleased." "Out of bed, Jukin?" says she, "You must be
out of your mind." "No, miss," I said. "Just you look at
that rug. When I brought your tray up, I set the edge of
it straight with that square on the carpet, & now it's
crept down half a foot. That rug always walks when
it's trodden on, but it can't walk of itself, & there's been
nobody up here since we started dinner, I can take my
oath of that." And then I look round, & there's the mistress
standing at the door, & dreadful while she was.

"What's all this, Jukin?" says Mrs Fastove. And I says,
"I'm happy to say, madam, as the young lady has recovered
the use of her limbs." And with that I went out & left them to
it, only I called Ludovic & said, "Madam wants you up in
Miss Blazey's room." And when he got up there, I heard the
young lady call out very pitiful, "Oh, Ludovic darling!"

And thinking it was a pity the joint should get
cold, I pops it back in a slow oven & sits down to a
bit of sewing.

Well, madam, it was all cleared up quite comfortable.
It seems Miss Blazey's trouble was of a hysterical sort,

after all she hadn't been much thought of at home or at school, & when she had her fall & was laid up, she enjoyed being the centre of attention & after that she went in play-acting, & presently, she look after they came to Mannering House, she got the idea of playing tricks, just to give herself importance, like little things at first, but when Ludovic came, he caught her at it & threatened to tell the mistress. Only then he got the idea of bettering himself, & he made love to the poor girl, slipping in of an evening when the mistress was out of the way; & the plot they made up between them was to frighten Mrs Fanshawe out of the house, so that the money should come to Miss Rosy, then he was to marry the young lady & hang his hat up in Mannering House for keeps. What with him hauling the heavy stuff about with his fishing-tackle & his ropes through the windows, & what with her sleeping out when he was in the dining-room, & banging the gong with her yo-yo affair tied on a long black elastic let down over the banisters they worked the trick easy enough but that old fool Mrs Pook helped them along (unconscious like) her silly talk about blood & murder — which the stain on the carpet turned out to be nothing worse than some kind of liqueur, & there never was no murder in the house at all, the gentleman having died in a fit.

111

It seems there was some trouble with Miss Brazey over Victoric. Really attached to him & his eyelashes & his Greek nose she was, poor girl — & of course, the minute it was all found out & there was no money with her, he backed out of it, not caring a snap of his fingers for her. She was really & truly ill after that, & Mrs Firestone took her abroad to get over the shock. When they came back to the house, she wanted me to stay on as head parlour-maid; but I made up my mind no the situation wouldn't suit me. Miss Brazey had took a kind of dis-like to me, & it wouldn't have been comfortable.

Mrs Firestone was very kind indeed — she was a nice lady — & behaved very generous. She gave me a present of the drawing-room rug, too, that's it over there. If you step on it, madam, you'll see that it moves under your weight. I showed it to a scientific gentleman who came to board with me. He was ever so interested, — said it was due to the hairs on it underneath being stiff & all lying the same way, so that they hooked into the carpet pile of the carpet. Scales, he said, has their scales set that way, & that's how they get along; but I never could abide them things.

with the tray, there's his nibs trying the door of Miss Brazey's own bedroom. "Well, & what next?" I said to him. "Miss Brazey wants something out of her room," says he, bold as brass. "Well," I says, "I'm the proper person to fetch it, not you. What is it?" "It's a blue silk scarf," says he. "All right," I says, "I'll get it. You buzz off, my lad," I says, seeing him still hanging about. Anybody'd think you'd done a murder in there & was looking for a chance to wipe off the finger-prints. That shut him up proper, & I thinks: "He's left something there he don't want us to find, & I'd like to know how that come about." So I went in & got the scarf & took it to Miss Brazey, who said, "Thank-you, Jukkin," without looking at me; & then back I went & stripped the bed down to the boards. And when I'd got the mattress & underlay off I got a torch & had a good look underneath. And there on the rim of the bed-frame under the spring, if you'll believe me, I found a little tin tray no bigger than a match-box & standing in it a little pyramid of ash, like the ghost of one of those incense-cones. It seemed a funny thing to me how anybody could a put it there & light it, without Miss Brazey noticing. You couldn't get at it by lifting the mattress, on account of the spring; you'd have to crawl under the bed.

Well, that made me think a bit, I can tell you, & I wondered if I'd find any more funny things about the room, I went all over it with a tooth-comb, as they say, + to cut a long story short, I shoved my hand down at the back of Miss Brazey's couch, between the head-rest + the seat, + out came an awful queer thing. It was just a small ball of wood tied on the end of a long black elastic, for all the world like one of these yo-yos the boys used to play with a few years ago. I put that back where I found it + left the little mound of ash just where it was + said nothing to nobody; only when I went downstairs again, I left the key of the room conspicuous-like, on the dresser.